MECHANIX ILLUSTRATED
HOW-TO-DO-IT
ENCYCLOPEDIA

Edited by the Combined Staffs of MECHANIX ILLUSTRATED
FAWCETT BOOKS and ELECTRONICS ILLUSTRATED

IN SIXTEEN VOLUMES

VOLUME 1

COMPLETE CONTENTS
AND INDEX IN VOLUME 16

Well-known reader services of Mechanix Illustrated are extended to readers of this encyclopedia to the extent of blueprint and plan offerings as indicated throughout the various
volumes. Inquiries relating to such services and communications regarding the editorial material in this encyclopedia should be directed to Fawcett Publications, Inc., Encyclopedia
Service, 67 West 44th Street, New York 36, N. Y. Printed in the United States of America.

GOLDEN PRESS • NEW YORK

MECHANIX ILLUSTRATED
HOW-TO-DO-IT
ENCYCLOPEDIA

Edited by the combined staffs of Fawcett Publications, Inc.

W. H. Fawcett, Jr. . . . . President

Roger Fawcett . . . . General Manager

Donald P. Hanson . Assistant Gen'l Manager

Gordon Fawcett . . . . . . Secretary-Treasurer

Roscoe Fawcett . . . . Circulation Director

Ralph Daigh . . . . Editorial Director

James B. Boynton . . . . . Advertising Director

Al Allard . . . . Art Director

Ralph Mattison . . . . . Associate Art Director

George H. Carl . . . . Production Director

MECHANIX ILLUSTRATED

WILLIAM L. PARKER . . . . **EDITOR**

Lawrence Sanders . . . . Feature Editor

Robert Brightman . . . Home and Shop Editor

Joseph D. Doyle . . . . Art Editor

Harvey Gardner . . . . Associate Editor

Dick Howe . . . . Associate Editor

John J. Smith . . . . Associate Editor

Adam Nott . . . . Associate Editor

J Robert Connor . . . . Assistant Editor

Helen S. Wolff . . . . Production Editor

Vincent Troiano . . . . Art Associate

Bob Spitzer . . . . Art Associate

ELECTRONICS ILLUSTRATED

ROBERT G. BEASON . . . . **EDITOR**

Larry Klein . . . . Technical Editor

Robert D. Freed . . . . Associate Editor

Murray Cooper . . . . Art Editor

Lou Rubsamen . . . . Art Associate

Elaine E. Sapoff . . . . Editorial Assistant

FAWCETT BOOKS

LARRY EISINGER . . . . . **EDITOR-IN-CHIEF**

George Tilton . . . . Managing Editor

Silvio Lembo . . . . Art Editor

Nick Carlucci . . . . Associate Art Editor

Dan Blue . . . . Associate Editor

Ray Gill . . . . Associate Editor

Joseph Piazza . . . . Associate Editor

Joseph Daffron . . . . Associate Editor

James Wyckoff . . . . Associate Editor

Adolphe Barreaux . . . . Associate Editor

W. Stevenson Bacon . . . . . Associate Editor

Susan B. Cole . . . . Editorial Assistant

Phyllis J. Bendremer . . . . . Production Editor

Benita Rockwood . . . . Assistant Prod. Editor

Harold E. Price . . . . Art Associate

Michael Gaynor . . . . Art Associate

John S. Selvaggio . . . . Art Associate

Bob Vatter . . . . Art Associate

Ed Kaplan . . . . Art Associate

Bernard Clorman . . . . Art Associate

Richard Rhodes . . . . Art Associate

Richard LoMonaco . . . . Art Associate

YOUR MECHANIX ILLUSTRATED HOW-TO-DO-IT ENCYCLOPEDIA

You are reading Volume I of the largest collection of do-it-yourself information ever assembled in a single work. The 3072 pages of this 16-volume encyclopedia were amassed from three principal sources to give you and your family the very finest how-to-do-it articles ever created:

MECHANIX ILLUSTRATED— Since 1928, the famous magazine that has presented the highest percentage of how-to subjects of any publication to do-it-yourself fans.

FAWCETT BOOKS—With over 400 titles, the largest illustrated library of home and hobby subjects. More than 40,000,000 copies of these authoritative how-to books have been printed.

ELECTRONICS ILLUSTRATED—The how-to magazine in the newest and most important of all scientific fields today.

On the next four pages the 403 major subjects covered in this encyclopedia are listed. Over 1,000,000 words of expert advice and instructions from nationally known authorities fully describe each subject. More than 10,000 detailed drawings and step-by-step photographs clearly illustrate every project, home repair or hobby. All projects and repairs have actually been fully completed and tested by an expert in the field.

We list below merely a few of these famous experts and their qualifications that will assure you of the finest how-to information obtainable.

AUTHORS and CONSULTANTS

FRED RUSSELL—
Automotive consultant; nationally syndicated columnist. Member: Society of Automotive Engineers; American Automobile Association.

HANK WIEAND BOWMAN—
Boating authority; syndicated newspaper columnist; author of 20 books, including "Encyclopedia of Outboard Motorboating."

ROBERT HERTZBERG—
Electronics expert; famous radio and TV author; Engineer, technician and former Editor-In-Chief of Mechanix Illustrated.

T. H. EVERETT—
Gardening authority; Curator of Education and Horticulturist of the New York Botanical Garden. World famous writer and lecturer on horticulture.

DONALD CARL HOEFLER—
Hi-Fi consultant; author, radio instructor, sound engineer and early associate with Major Edwin H. Armstrong, inventor of FM radio.

SIMON NATHAN—
Photography consultant; well known author, magazine and industrial photographer; former staff photographer, United Press Newspictures.

GRIFF BORGESON—
Hot rod and karting consultant; author of many books and articles on how-to subjects. Well-known hot rod and karting expert.

BERNARD GLADSTONE—
Do-It-Yourself expert; Home Improvement Editor of the New York Times; author of numerous best-selling how-to books.

CLARENCE MARTIN—
Home and shop expert; regularly published author in Mechanix Illustrated. Consultant in tool and workshop techniques.

LLOYD MALLAN—
Science consultant; well-known author of many books and magazine articles in fields of astronomy, missiles, electronics and space science.

WALTER IAN FISCHMAN—
How-To authority. Regularly published columnist for New York Daily News. Author of hundreds of books and articles on how-to subjects.

R. J. DeCRISTOFORO—
Building and power tools consultant; outstanding writer on home craftsman subjects. Best-selling author of power tool books.

ART MARGOLIS—
Television repair expert; a professional TV authority; author of TV books and articles. Regularly published TV repair department in Popular Science.

HENRY CLARK—
How-To artist and designer; work has appeared in many hundreds of books and magazine articles; pioneer in detailed, do-it-yourself diagrams.

THE 403 MAJOR SUBJECTS COVERED IN THIS ENCYCLOPEDIA

This alphabetical list indicates only the more important categories. A complete, cross-referenced index covering all 3072 pages will be found in Volume 16.

A

AIR CONDITIONING
ALARMS
APPLIANCE REPAIR,
    Tools
    Fans and Mixers
    Vacuum Cleaners
    Dishwashers
    Washing Machines
    Freezers
    Toasters, Grills
    Electric Irons
    Clothes Dryers
AQUARIUMS
ARCHERY
ASTRONOMY
ATTICS
AUTOMOBILES,
    Brakes
    Differential
    Wheel Bearings
    Carburetor
    Suspension
    Lights
    Wheel Alignment
    Spark Plugs
    Starting
    Noise
    Motor Miss
    Trouble Shooting

B

BARBECUES
BASEMENTS,
    Planning
    Wall Paneling
    Pine Finish
    Floors, Ceilings
    Stairs, Entrances

BATHROOMS
BAY WINDOW
BED
BEDROOMS
BENCHES
BICYCLE RACK
BIRD BATH
BOATING,
    Dock
    Railway
    Trailer
    Canvas Top
    Calking, Painting
    Sailing
    Motor Cart
    Windshield
    Detachable Cabin
    Hull Repair
    Child's Runabout
    Rowboat
    Racing Runabout
    Outboard Runabout
    Cabin Cruiser
    Kayak
    Ice Boat
BOOKCASES
BOOT BIN
BRICK
BUFFET
BUILT-INS

C

CABANA
CABINETS,
    Kitchen
    Record
    Sewing
    Spice
CABINS
CALKING

CAMPING,
    Choosing Tent
    Campsite
    Fire
    Cooking
    Survival
    Dangers
CANOE
CAROUSEL
CARPENTRY,
    Tools
    Wood
    Fastenings
    Adhesives
    Joists, Studding
    Roofs, Rafters
    Framing Square
    Outside Finish
    Windows, Doors
    Inside Finish
CARPORT
CARTS
CASTERS
CEILINGS
CERAMICS,
    Tools
    Clays
    Molds
    Casting
    Potter's Wheel
    Glazes
    Kilns
    Firing
CHAIRS,
    Dining
    Lawn
    Child's
    Cord
CHAISE
CHESTS
CHIMNEY
CHRISTMAS LIGHTS

CIRCUIT TESTER
CLEANING CART
CLOSETS,
    Linen
    Cleaning
CLOTHES CABINET
CLOTHES RACKS
CONCRETE
CONCRETE BLOCK
COUCHES
CRIBS
CURBS

D

DECK
DESKS,
    Office
    Boy's
    Housewife's
    Wardrobe
DISH CABINET
DIVIDERS
DOORBELLL
DOORS
DRAINING
DRAWERS
DRAWING
DRIVEWAYS

E

ELECTRICAL REPAIRS,
    Wiring
    Tools, Testers
    Wire Joints
    Cable, Conduit
    Safety
    Third Wire
    Lights
    Bells

Coffee Maker
Cords
Re-cording Lamp
Bowl Heaters
Fluorescent Lights
Silent Switch
Extending Outlet
Furnace
Air Conditioner
Batteries
Outdoors
Clocks
ELECTRONICS,
    Lock
    AC Battery
    Sun Powered Receiver
    Control Center
    Auto Tachometer
    Fire Alarm
    Time Delay Switch
    Intercom
    Headlight Switch
    Voice Switch
    Signal Splitter
    Short Wave
    Megaphone
    Skywatcher
    Failproof Alarm
    Recording Beeper
ENTRANCEWAYS
EXCAVATING

F

FENCES
FIREPLACES
FISHING BOX
FLAGSTONE
FLASHING
FLOORS
FOUNDATION

FOYER
FRAMING
FURNITURE

G

GAMES
GARAGES
GARDEN CADDY
GARDENING,
    Planning
    Soils
    Planting Trees
    Shrubs
    Evergreens
    Groundcovers
    Hedges
    Vines
    Annuals
    Biennials
    Perennials
    Bulbs
    Rock Gardens
    Garden Pool
    Vegetables
    Fruits
    Herbs
    Shade
    Hotbeds
    Sowing Seeds
    Cuttings
    Dividing
    Layering
    Grafting
    Winter Protection
    Pruning
GAUGES
GEIGER COUNTER
GLUES
GREEN HOUSE

GUITAR AMPLIFIER
GUTTERS

H

HASSOCKS
HEADBOARDS
HEATING
HI-FI,
    Starting Out
    Packages
    Kits
    TV, Radio
    Tape Recorder
    Maintenance
    Cabinet
    Speaker
HORSE, HANDYMAN'S
HOT RODS
HOUSE PLANTS,
    Light
    Temperature
    Atmosphere
    Water
    Soil
    Bugs
    Transplanting
    Dividing
    Seeds
    Cuttings

I

INCINERATOR

J

JOINTS
JOISTS
JUNGLE GYM

K

KARTING
KITCHENS

L

LAMP POST
LAMPS
LAUNDRY CART
LAVATORY
LAWNS,
    Grading
    Draining
    Soil Conditioning
    Seed
    Turf
    Stolons
    Sprigs
    Plugs
LAZY SUSAN
LIE DETECTOR
LINOLEUM

M

MANTEL
MASONRY
METRONOME
MOTORS
MOVIE TITLER

N

NIGHT STAND
NUTCRACKER

O

OUTDOOR UTILITIES

P

PAINTING,
    Interior
    Exterior
    Washing
    Screens
PANELING
PANTRY
PARTITIONS
PATIOS
PERISCOPE
PHOTOGRAPHY,
    Darkroom
    Negatives
    Reduction
    Contact Printing
    Enlargers
    Varigam
    Printing
    Short Stop, Hypo
    Print Finishing
    Photo Bar
    Photo Fountain
    Photo Corner
    Photo Wall
    Picture Frame
    Kitchen Darkroom
    Print Washer
    Print Dryer
PICNICS
PLANTERS
PLASTER
PLATFORM
PLAY AREAS
PLAYHOUSES
PLUMBING,
    Pipe
    Tools
    Copper Tubing
    Galvanized Steel

WHAT YOU SHOULD KNOW ABOUT

air conditioning for new homes

Better health, more comfort, can be yours with modern air conditioning.

ROOM DIFFUSER, seen in ceiling above light fixture, provides cool, dehumidified, filtered air for the area it serves—here, dining room.

INSTALLATION of room air conditioners through the wall is logical method in new home construction. It keeps windows free and uncluttered.

Frigidaire

DRAW a line across the country at the latitude of lower Pennsylvania. Any house built now below that line without air conditioning will be *obsolete in 10 years*. Fortunately, it is the FHA which has arrived at this conclusion, for it means that cooling equipment of all kinds may now be included in a mortgage, and thus acquired with a minimum of financial stress. Even if you live above that line, the FHA will back you, for they have decided that the inclusion of air conditioning in *all* new homes is a good thing and should be encouraged.

New simplified packaged units, recently devised prefabricated glass-fiber ducts, and improved add-on techniques make it possible to acquire a system for an 1800-square-foot house for as little as $600 to $900. Two men can often do the installation in a day. You can install it yourself —this is a central system that will cool *every part* of your house. Its upkeep? No less an authority than the FHA concurs that the savings air conditioning makes possible more than offset its operating costs.

Is it worth-while? Home air conditioning has come a long way from the early days of overcooled theaters and the thermal shock they inflicted. We know now that a 15-degree differential in temperature is the maximum usually desirable, and accurate controls assure the comfort we want.

We know, too, that health is never harmed by summer cooling. On the con-trary, there are fewer colds and smaller doctor bills. The filtered air benefits allergies, asthma, sinus, hay fever. Control of temperature and humidity is a godsend to the aged and the invalid. Heart conditions and high blood pressure escape the stresses brought on by oppressive heat.

Housekeeping is easier. The cleaner air means less time spent pushing a vacuum, fewer trips to the dry cleaners, lighter loads for the washing machine. The need for reupholstering, redecorating, repainting becomes more infrequent. Clothes hold their shape better, and mildew and rust become almost forgotten words.

It will improve your disposition. When you're less fatigued, things just naturally look brighter. The children can have their daytime naps and hot meals, and be put to bed on schedule in shade-darkened rooms. You'll sleep longer and better, too, awake refreshed and free of hot weather nerves.

You can forget about screens, and leave the storm windows up all year around.

Best of all, central air conditioning is something you can afford. Like its long-lived cousin, the refrigerator, a conditioner can be expected to last 20 to 25 years or more. That brings its per-year cost down mighty low.

For any house. No matter what style your home is, ranch, two-story, Colonial or contemporary, central air conditioning is easily installed. The equipment won't take up valuable space either. It can go in out-of-the-way waste space.

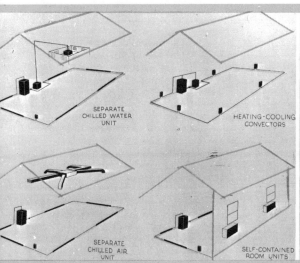

Permaglas

FOR HOT WATER heating system in a new home, here are four possible ways to provide a full, year-'round cooling system along with the heat.

SELF-CONTAINED central air conditioning units, such as this one, have all components in single package; eliminates need for special plumbing.

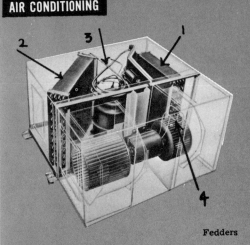

Fedders

CONDITIONER works like this: Compressed refrigerant evaporates in coils (1). Its temperature drops with evaporation, absorbs heat from room air blown over coils. The heat is disposed of in coils (2) where refrigerant is pressured by compressor (3). Blower (4) disperses extra heat.

FIBER DUCTS, leading from the self-contained unit placed in the attic, distribute cool air through ceiling diffusers to the rooms below.

But there's no denying that the easiest and most economical way to get year-'round whole-house air conditioning is when you build. If that's done, the house can be designed and oriented for best operation, and this can mean savings both in the size of equipment and in the cost of the house itself.

If you can't see your way clear to have summer cooling included when building, by all means *make provision for its easy adding later.* Manufacturers have designed equipment for just such circumstances, and your savings over starting from scratch will be substantial.

If your house is to have a forced warm air system, cooling can be a part of it. This costs less than having a completely separate cooling system, for your regular heating ductwork, filters and furnace blower do double duty for cooling. You can get year-'round air conditioners in the same variety of styles in which you buy a furnace alone—high or low boy, horizontal or counterflow. The units can be installed in basement, attic, crawlspace, or in a closet located in the living area. The cooling coil is located in the furnace's outlet. From the coil small copper pipes connect to a weatherproof refrigeration section set in the yard, garage, carport, or basement.

If you plan to add cooling later to your heating system, there are things to watch for. Be sure ducts that require insulation get it when they are installed. They may be inaccessible later. *Be sure your ducts and blower are big enough to handle cooling.* This is especially important if you live in a mild-winter zone. *Be sure you get a perimeter heating system,* and diffusers that will work as well for cooling as they do for heating.

You can get a hot water system that will also work for cooling your house. For cooling, chilled water is circulated instead of hot water. Instead of radiators you'll have cooling-heating units, each with its own thermostat. These systems are more expensive than year-'round forced air systems. The minimum cost for an average one-story, 7-room house with basement, is likely to run $1500 above the cost of the heating alone.

Separate systems. If the problems of combining cooling with your heating are knotty, it may be cheaper to plan on a completely separate cooling system. The simplest kind of separate system uses a single, self-contained unit. It is, in effect, an oversize room conditioner equipped with prefab glass-fiber ducts to distribute the cooled, cleaned, dehumidified air where it is wanted.

In a long, rambling ranch, two such units can be installed, one serving the living area, the other the sleeping zone. In a two-story house, one unit may be installed in the basement to serve the first floor, another in the attic to cool the second. In each case, having separate systems for living and

A SEPARATE condensing unit, remote from the cooling coils, serves two functions: it reduces the operating noise considerably, saves space.

A COPPER TUBE carries the compressed refrigerant from the remote, air-cooled condensing unit to the cooling coils which are located in house.

sleeping areas has the advantage of permitting individual zone control.

The heat pump. One of the more remarkable of the new cooling systems is one that can be switched to heating. As you know, a conditioner makes indoor air cool by pumping the heat out of it and then releasing this heat outdoors. A relatively simple switching arrangement reverses the cycle so that the machine literally runs backward, and the heat is extracted from outdoor air and turned indoors.

Up until recently, this heat pump method of warming air was efficient only in areas of mild winters and when outside temperatures were above 40 degrees. Now, the machine has been improved to a point where it is generally more economical than oil heat at temperatures down to 15 degrees. You can get this added heating feature for as little as $200 more than the price of cooling alone.

Consider it as a standby setup, at negligible cost, for those emergencies when the furnace quits, a blizzard holds up fuel delivery, or for cool summer mornings or evenings when you don't want to start up your whole heating plant.

What size conditioner? How large a cooling unit you need, and the method of its installation, depends on a variety of factors. Among other things, besides the nature of your house and how much heat finds its way into its various rooms from the outside, it will depend upon your

THIS IS an evaporating unit about to be set into a crawl space (above). Its ducting is much simpler than that required for heating. Below, the same drain serving house's downspout carries condensate (condensed moisture) away. Condensate results from warm air losing moisture as it cools.

personal habits and the makeup of your family. Families with children usually don't want the house quite so cool. If you are a party thrower, you may need added capacity. The body is a heat machine, and 20 to 25 guests can easily double your cooling load.

Cooling requirements are best expressed in terms of BTU's. A BTU is a unit of heat, and the BTU rating of a conditioner refers to how much heat your machine can pump *out* of your house in an hour. A very rough rule of thumb is that, under favorable conditions, you'll need 15 BTU's of cooling for every square foot of your house. This is if outdoor temperatures have a high average of 95 degrees. You'll need more if the high

HEAVY INSULATION is required on pipes in a chilled-water air-conditioning system. In this system, each room unit has its own thermostat.

IN THIS installation, condensing unit remains outside (1), while the cooling coils (2) slide through the wall into plenum of furnace (3).

Frigidaire

average is above that, less if it's below.

Coolers are also rated by tons. A ton of cooling compares to the cooling you get by melting a ton of ice. By accepted definition, a 1-ton conditioner will provide 12,000 BTU of cooling in one hour.

You may find a conditioner rated by horsepower. It is generally an inaccurate method of rating, for the horsepower is that of the compressor motor, and many other components beside it determine how much cooling you'll get. A 1-hp conditioner, for example, may vary in effectiveness from under 8,000 BTU to well over 10,000 BTU.

The safest procedure is to let your builder estimate the size of the unit you need, rather than trying to do this yourself.

Don't urge your builder to give you a little extra cooling capacity just to be sure you have enough. Better to have your equipment slightly undersized than too big. Here's why:

Reducing humidity is often as important as cooling. An oversize unit will cool off your house quickly, then shut down for a long period. Before it cycles on again, humidity can build up and make you uncomfortable even though the temperature is still low. With a unit of the right size, a compressor will run continuously during hot weather, reducing humidity as evenly as it does temperature.

Money-saving tips. Attention to details can cut in half the size unit you need and pare operating expense proportionately. A well-designed, 1200-square-foot house can be comfortably cooled and heated for as little as $128 a year, or $11 a month.

If you have a house which heat doesn't penetrate easily, your unit will have less heat to remove. Keep the direct sun from reaching the house and you've won the first battle. In a new house, generous roof overhangs are a logical and effective solution. If the house you plan to buy or build won't have big overhangs, you can still do a fair job of keeping the sun off walls and windows with properly designed trellises, fences and awnings.

Shade trees, too, are a big help, so keep them if you can. Drawn blinds and draperies do some good, but not nearly as much as shading devices on the outside of the house.

The more directly the sun strikes walls and roof, the greater its heat impact. The way a house is set on its lot can therefore influence how much cooling you're going to need. A shift in the walls, or a change in the roof slope, so the sun hits them more obliquely, can save you money.

You can use heat-absorbing glass to stop the sun, double glass and insulated glass to combat condensation. *Restrict large glass areas to the north and south sides of the house.* They're easier to shade there. An attic space above insulation makes a house easier to cool. You'll even gain by putting

HEATING-COOLING convector looks like radiator, has coils through which cold or hot water passes, depending on whether heating or cooling is wanted.

HEAT PUMP is a heating-cooling unit which can be installed in a basement, crawl-space or attic. Notice the separate compressor, in extreme right.

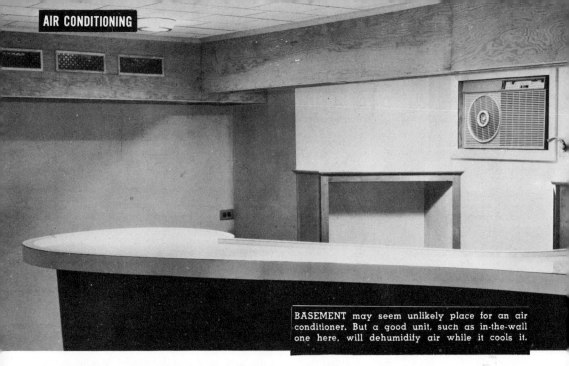

BASEMENT may seem unlikely place for an air conditioner. But a good unit, such as in-the-wall one here, will dehumidify air while it cools it.

your water heater outside the conditioned space, and using an electric range instead of a gas one. Gas adds to the moisture load.

Insulate, weatherstrip, double-glaze to the maximum. In insulation, the numbers to remember are 6-4-2. They stand for 6 inches of mineral wool insulation in the ceiling, 4 inches in the side walls, 2 inches in the floors. Such extra-thick insulation not only permits a much smaller cooling installation, but will continue to reduce operating expenses both in heating and cooling. A light-colored roof will reduce sun heat by 50 per cent.

It costs two to three times as much to remove a BTU in summer as it does to add one in winter, so every solitary BTU is worth attention. You'll foil them in droves, along with their pal humidity, by having and using a kitchen range exhaust fan, a bathroom ventilator for when you shower, and an outside vent for the clothes drier.

Keeping conditioners quiet. It's no use pretending that all conditioners are quiet, but the noise they produce can be kept to a minimum. Good workmanship is important in the installation, so if you're doing your own contracting, don't award the job on the basis of price alone.

Avoid attic placement directly above a bedroom. Avoid installations on wood platforms. There will be less structural vibration if a unit is placed over a load-bearing partition.

Acoustical conditioning of the attic will help prevent sound buildup. Treatment may consist of no more than acoustical fiberboard on the ceiling, or fiberboard baffles placed vertically to break up sound waves.

Duct insulation dampens the sound of air movement. It also prevents excessive duct heat-gain in unconditioned spaces and condensation on the duct surfaces.

Some brands of air conditioners are quieter than others. Listen to them run and ask the dealer what the manufacturer has done to make his unit quiet. An astounding number of purchasers never even ask to hear the machine they buy.

Does the unit have two compressors or one? Two compressors are likely to be less disturbing, for one of them will be running continuously and a sustained level of sound is not nearly as annoying as on-off cycling. Having a split system, with compressor and blower separated, is likely to be quieter than where both compressor and blower are right in the house. You'll still have the sound of the blower, but at least the compressor noises will be isolated.

The new gas-fired air conditioners are especially quiet for they have no compressor, motor, or valves to cause noise or vibration. Aside from the blower, there are no moving parts. It is the one type of air conditioner that requires no special wiring, for both heating and cooling are accomplished by the use of one fuel, gas.

Room Coolers. Where cooling needs are limited, room units are ideal, though if you need three or more of them you will almost certainly get by for less with a central system.

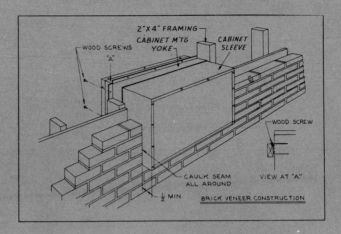

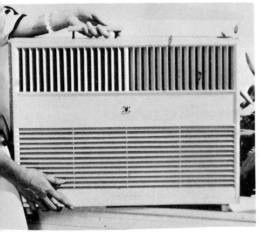

CABINET SLEEVE, like this one, can be installed in wall of a house during its construction. When you are ready to buy an air conditioner, it can be simply installed in sleeve.

Frigidaire

NEW PORTABLE air conditioners cool, dehumidify or heat. They are handsome, light in weight and can be carried from room to room as needed.

Carrier

The most popular place for a room cooler used to be the bedroom. Now the trend is to live cool rather than sleep cool and more initial purchases are for living areas.

Room units are becoming smaller, slimmer, and at the same time more efficient. Some are now only half the size of their previous models. Conditioners designed to operate on regular 115 volt house current used to be of low capacity. Not any more. Now you can get 1½-hp compressors which operate on that voltage. Any unit requiring 7½ amperes or less current can be plugged into a 115-volt outlet, though many city codes require that the line be for the conditioner's exclusive use.

One new development has been to get more out of compressors by running them twice as fast as formerly. Another is the design of units which, according to their manufacturers, will cool two and even three rooms. Making big news, too, are portable conditioners, adaptable for cooling, heating and dehumidifying.

The smaller portables weigh about 60 pounds, and the idea is to move one about the house, plugging it in where you need it. Have it in the living room in the evening, take it with you to the bedroom when you retire. But don't expect miracles. Portables equipped with ¼-hp compressors are low in cooling capacity, and you are likely to feel little effect unless you are sitting in their direct path. It may take 5 or 6 hours of continuous operation to cool even a small room. Larger portable of ¾ and 1 hp have good capacity, but may present moving problems.

Other new units with wall-thin styling eliminate objectionable overhang both on the inside and outside of the house. These in-the-wall coolers are the most compact of all air conditioners. Just as you can make provision when you build for adding central cooling later, so you can allow for future installation of these in-the-wall conditioners. A special shell, supplied with covering plates, is built into the wall and wiring provided. When you decide to have a unit installed, the chassis slides right into place.

Switch the unit on, and you can forget about the weather. It will keep it pegged at the temperature you select, even if it has to jump from cooling to heating. Most of the better window units these days do that. They're designed to earn their way 12 months of the year. ●

IN YOUR PRESENT HOME . . .

install a central air conditioning system

Year-'round comfort can be yours for a fraction of the price you'd expect to pay . . . of course, it takes time and effort on your part.

COMPLETE home air conditioning is now within easy reach of most household budgets, thanks to an enterprising manufacturer who realizes that the do-it-yourself market is here to stay. The firm has brought out a complete air conditioning system in kit form. It enables the average handy man to do the job himself, with a little help on the heavier parts of the work.

In addition to selling you the unit, the manufacturer's local dealer also inspects the home in which the system is to be installed, just to make certain the unit is ideally suited to the home. The dealer will also handle all service calls.

The enterprising manufacturer is Chrysler Corporation, and the product is the Airtemp two-horsepower (or three-horsepower) waterless air conditioner and related accessories. The two-horsepower system is intended primarily for single story homes having a floor area up to about 1125 square feet, a gable roof and an accessible attic. The three-horsepower unit can handle one story homes up to 1800 square feet, depending upon the type, the amount of insulation the home has, the size and location of the windows, the climate, the size of the roof overhang, and, of course, the manner in which the home is oriented in relation to the sun, on its plot of land.

Introduced in the late spring of 1956, the two-horsepower unit proved an immediate success during the summer that followed. The heart of the system is a self-contained cooler, completely factory-assembled, charged and ready for immediate use upon installation. Extremely compact, it measures 29½ inches wide, 23¼ inches high and 36¾ inches long, and it can be maneuvered readily through ordinary doors and passageways in a home. It weighs 300 pounds; a little too much for one man to handle, but no problem for two.

In conventional central cooling installations, the sheet metal ducts that circulate the air represent a large part of the original expense. In the new Airtemp system, you make your own ducts quickly and easily out of ¾-inch fiberglass boards, which are coated on one side with aluminum foil. Shipped flat, they assemble into two sizes: 10 by 14 inches cross section by 4 feet long, and 8 by 8 inches cross section and 6 feet long. The boards are preformed with three V-shaped grooves evenly spaced along their length, and it takes only minutes to fold them square and to bind the one joined corner with tape and cement, which are furnished. The ducts thus formed are light and very rigid, and can be

CONDITIONER, an air-cooled unit, is set in an opening in the gable of the house, just under the attic window. This is Gelormini home (opp. pg.).

HIP ROOF, rather than gable roof as described in the story, requires dormer to be built out of the roof (as below), in which conditioner is set.

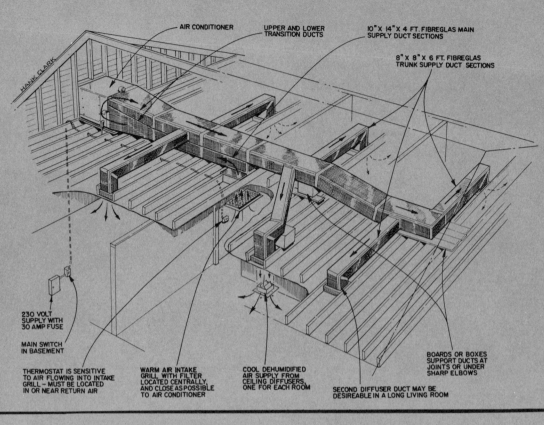

HANK CLARK

AIR CONDITIONER

UPPER AND LOWER
TRANSITION DUCTS

10" X 14" X 4 FT. FIBREGLAS MAIN
SUPPLY DUCT SECTIONS

8" X 8" X 6 FT. FIBREGLAS
TRUNK SUPPLY DUCT SECTIONS

230 VOLT
SUPPLY WITH
30 AMP FUSE

MAIN SWITCH
IN BASEMENT

THERMOSTAT IS SENSITIVE
TO AIR FLOWING INTO INTAKE
GRILL – MUST BE LOCATED
IN OR NEAR RETURN AIR

WARM AIR INTAKE
GRILL WITH FILTER
LOCATED CENTRALLY,
AND CLOSE AS POSSIBLE
TO AIR CONDITIONER

COOL DEHUMIDIFIED
AIR SUPPLY FROM
CEILING DIFFUSERS,
ONE FOR EACH ROOM

SECOND DIFFUSER DUCT MAY BE
DESIREABLE IN A LONG LIVING ROOM

BOARDS OR BOXES
SUPPORT DUCTS AT
JOINTS OR UNDER
SHARP ELBOWS

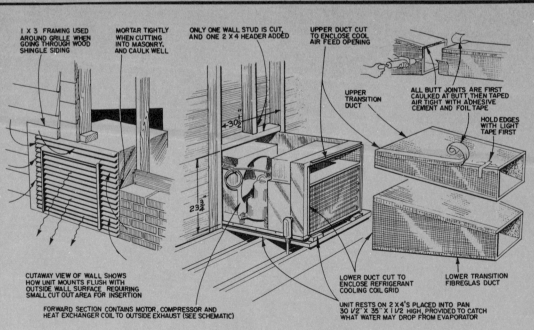

1 X 3 FRAMING USED
AROUND GRILLE WHEN
GOING THROUGH WOOD
SHINGLE SIDING

MORTAR TIGHTLY
WHEN CUTTING
INTO MASONRY,
AND CAULK WELL

ONLY ONE WALL STUD IS CUT,
AND ONE 2 X 4 HEADER ADDED

UPPER DUCT CUT
TO ENCLOSE COOL
AIR FEED OPENING

UPPER
TRANSITION
DUCT

ALL BUTT JOINTS ARE FIRST
CAULKED AT BUTT, THEN TAPED
AIR TIGHT WITH ADHESIVE
CEMENT AND FOIL TAPE

HOLD EDGES
WITH LIGHT
TAPE FIRST

←30½→

23¾"

CUTAWAY VIEW OF WALL SHOWS
HOW UNIT MOUNTS FLUSH WITH
OUTSIDE WALL SURFACE REQUIRING
SMALL CUT OUT AREA FOR INSERTION

FORWARD SECTION CONTAINS MOTOR, COMPRESSOR AND
HEAT EXCHANGER COIL TO OUTSIDE EXHAUST (SEE SCHEMATIC)

LOWER DUCT CUT TO
ENCLOSE REFRIGERANT
COOLING COIL GRID

LOWER TRANSITION
FIBREGLAS DUCT

UNIT RESTS ON 2 X 4'S PLACED INTO PAN
30 1/2" X 35" X 1 1/2 HIGH, PROVIDED TO CATCH
WHAT WATER MAY DROP FROM EVAPORATOR

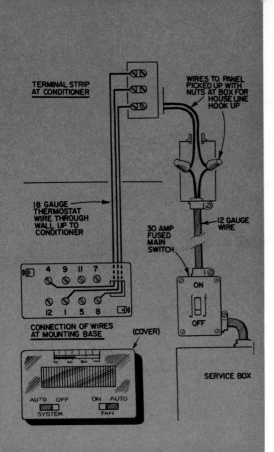

Diagram labels:
TERMINAL STRIP AT CONDITIONER

WIRES TO PANEL PICKED UP WITH NUTS AT BOX FOR HOUSE LINE HOOK UP

18 GAUGE THERMOSTAT WIRE THROUGH WALL UP TO CONDITIONER

30 AMP FUSED MAIN SWITCH

12 GAUGE WIRE

4 9 11 7
12 1 5 8

CONNECTION OF WIRES AT MOUNTING BASE

(COVER)

ON
OFF

SERVICE BOX

AUTO OFF ON AUTO
SYSTEM FAN

FIBERGLAS ducts of Airtemp system are packed flat, as in photo above. They are coated with aluminum foil and scored lengthwise for folding.

SCORED BOARDS fold up simply to form ducts. Boards are ¾ inch thick. This Fiberglas duct is six feet long and has an 8x8-inch cross section.

JOINT of duct is closed with self-adhering tape, then final sealing is done with tape of aluminum foil and special cement. It's all part of the kit.

shaped or cut to length with an ordinary carpenter's saw or even a sharp knife.

Also included in the kit are five ceiling diffusers or registers, a return air grille with integral filter and a wall thermostat. Being waterless, the cooler unit itself must be mounted in the side of the gable, so that the heat extracted from the house air can be blown into the atmosphere. The ducts are laid on the attic floor or beams, and the diffusers and the return grille are mounted in rectangular openings cut into the ceilings of the rooms below.

The electrical requirements are normal for the two-horsepower unit; a 230-volt, 60-cycle, single-phase line, minimum wire size No. 12. The compressor and blower motors take a total of a little more than 13 amperes. A 24-volt transformer for operation of the thermostat is built into the cooler box.

In units larger than two horsepower, 208-volt models are being produced, for use in homes supplied with four-wire, three-phase, 120/180-volt power. No units are made for 115 volts, because the line current at this voltage would be twice that at 230, and the new line itself would have to be so heavy that it could not be installed economically.

If there are three wires coming into your house from the power company's lines, you already have 115/230-volt service. Check with the utility to determine if this can deliver the necessary current for the air conditioner in addition to the present load of the regular household appliances. At any event, it is necessary to run a separate line, with its own fuse or circuit breaker, from the meter.

The home in which the installation pictured on these pages was made is owned by Thomas Gelormini of Gibbstown, New Jersey. His is just the kind of house the Chrysler engineers must have had in mind when they designed the Model 1118. The Gelormini home consists of a living room, a kitchen, two bedrooms and a bathroom, all on one floor. It has a well-insulated attic, with a window at each end, and this is accessible through a short flight of stairs leading out of a bedroom closet. Electric

WOODEN SUPPORT for an attic duct takes load off the short, vertical duct that goes through attic floor to ceiling diffuser in room below.

ROCK WOOL insulation is stuffed into opening that leads to a ceiling diffuser. Note that the duct feeding diffuser rests directly on the floor.

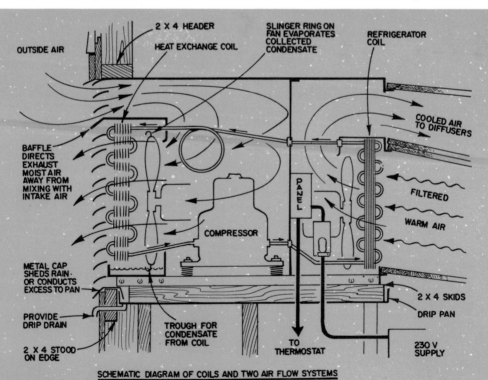

SCHEMATIC DIAGRAM OF COILS AND TWO AIR FLOW SYSTEMS

service is what is required—115/230 volts.

Following the manufacturer's instructions implicitly, Mr. Gelormini and his son Frank did the whole installation in the equivalent of two working days. In advance of the delivery of the kit, they cut an opening in the gable, just under one of the attic windows. They were all ready when Mr. Harry Wohlrab, the local Airtemp dealer from nearby Paulsboro, called up and said, "The shipment's here. When can I come over with it?"

SCRAP pieces of wood are used to trim off the floor opening for the short section of duct that leads to the ceiling diffuser in the room below.

OWNER surveys the duct system in his attic. Two horizontal ducts nearest him are raised above the floor level to accommodate a needed return duct.

MOUNTED into the outside wall of the attic, Airtemp 2-ton conditioner is readily accessible for inspection and servicing. The L-shaped fitting in lower right carries 230-volt AC power lines up.

As part of his service as the selling dealer, Mr. Wohlrab and a helper rolled the 300-pound cooler in on a dolly and also wormed it up the attic steps. That was the hardest part of the job, all agreed.

The Gelorminis installed two ceiling diffusers in the living room, the largest room of the house, and one each in the kitchen and the bedrooms. They put the return grille in the ceiling of a small passageway that connects the bedrooms and the bathroom.

"We had no trouble of any kind," reports Mr. Gelormini. "When we finished the last duct we went downstairs, closed all the windows and turned on the line switch and the thermostat. Within ten minutes we could feel the difference, and after half an hour the house was really comfortable. During the worst parts of the summer, when the dampness in the air was as bad as the heat, the inside of the house was not only cool but dry. We now get a good night's sleep." Mrs. Gelormini is happy with the system for an extra reason. "The house stays cleaner," she says.

Operating expense is nominal. The Gelorminis figure that the air conditioning costs them only about $9 a month during the summer, over their previous bills. Their local rate is 2¾ cents per kilowatt hour.

"That's cheap," they say. "In fact, it's almost saving money for us, because this way we can stay home and watch television instead of driving around looking for a cool spot."

While the majority of homes can use either the two- or three-horsepower job, suppose you have a split-level home or a two-story dwelling that requires greater tonnage. The answer is easy!

Install two separate systems. This is not only simpler to accomplish than one very large system, but in most cases gives more uniform cooling. If the ducts of a single system are extended too far from the cooler unit, the last diffusers get only a weak stream of air. The identical trouble, at the other end of the thermometer, is common with many heating systems. The Airtemp manufacturers know of a two-story house with one attic-mounted Model 1118 serving the upstairs bedrooms, a second unit in the basement cooling the kitchen and the dining room, and a third, also in the basement, cooling the sun porch and a large living room. Far from being extravagant, this arrangement is actually economical in that the temperature in each area can be controlled to suit conditions there. For example, the kitchen and dining sections need steady cooling during the preparation and serving of meals. At this time, the bedrooms and the living room need little if any cooling. At night, the

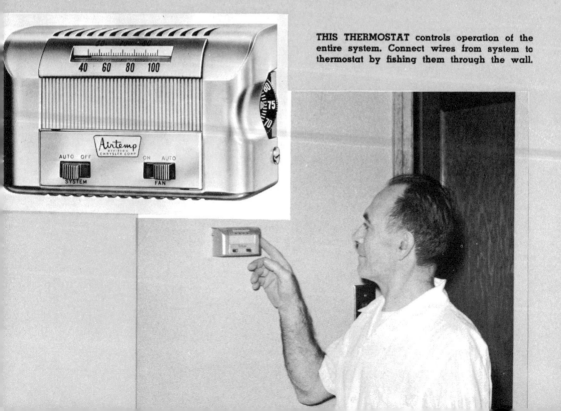

THIS THERMOSTAT controls operation of the entire system. Connect wires from system to thermostat by fishing them through the wall.

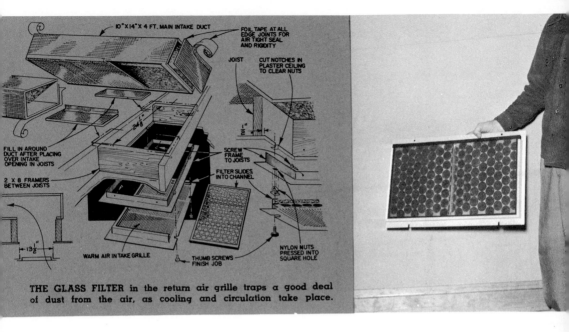

10"X14"X4 FT. MAIN INTAKE DUCT

FOIL TAPE AT ALL EDGE JOINTS FOR AIR TIGHT SEAL AND RIGIDITY

JOIST

CUT NOTCHES IN PLASTER CEILING TO CLEAR NUTS

FILL IN AROUND DUCT AFTER PLACING OVER INTAKE OPENING IN JOISTS

SCREW FRAME TO JOISTS

FILTER SLIDES INTO CHANNEL

2 X 8 FRAMERS BETWEEN JOISTS

13½"

WARM AIR IN TAKE GRILLE

THUMB SCREWS FINISH JOB

NYLON NUTS PRESSED INTO SQUARE HOLE

THE GLASS FILTER in the return air grille traps a good deal of dust from the air, as cooling and circulation take place.

THIS is the return air grille of the Airtemp system. The cover of the grille is held by thumb screws, readily removable for servicing needs.

HOMEOWNER who installed this system points to the circuit breaker of separate 230-volt line run from service box to the air conditioner in attic.

HERE is how one of the Airtemp ceiling diffusers looks when it has been disassembled. The components shown here are called deflecting vanes.

COMPLETED diffuser, with last piece being put on. The air spreads out evenly from between the overhanging edges on perimeter of square sections.

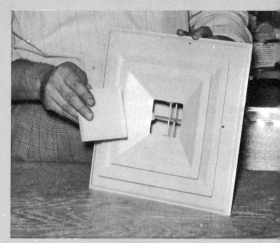

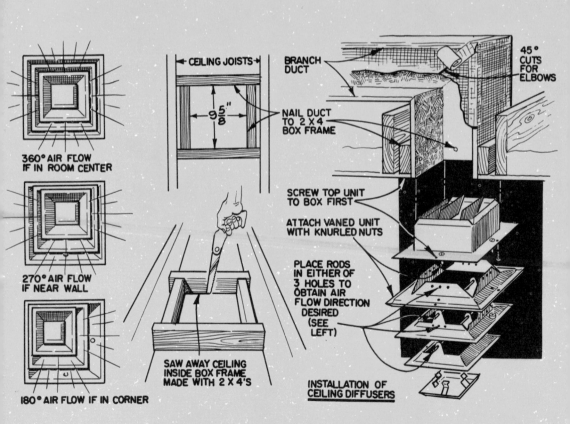

360° AIR FLOW IF IN ROOM CENTER

270° AIR FLOW IF NEAR WALL

180° AIR FLOW IF IN CORNER

← CEILING JOISTS →

9 5/8"

SAW AWAY CEILING INSIDE BOX FRAME MADE WITH 2 X 4'S

BRANCH DUCT

NAIL DUCT TO 2 X 4 BOX FRAME

45° CUTS FOR ELBOWS

SCREW TOP UNIT TO BOX FIRST

ATTACH VANED UNIT WITH KNURLED NUTS

PLACE RODS IN EITHER OF 3 HOLES TO OBTAIN AIR FLOW DIRECTION DESIRED (SEE LEFT)

INSTALLATION OF CEILING DIFFUSERS

DIFFUSERS and registers come in these different styles. The two in background are for baseboard or wall mounting; one in front is for the floor.

lower floor can be shut down altogether, and only the attic unit left on to serve the bedrooms.

Although the project discussed here has been the air conditioning of an existing home, this seems like a good place to point out that it is every bit as applicable to a house that is just being built. In fact, putting the system into an unfinished new home is even simpler! The important difference is that all ductwork and wiring for the system should be installed before any finishing and painting work. This will eliminate the need for cutting into walls, ceilings and floors and will make a neater job of it. Just consider the ducting and wiring as you do windows and doors—as an integral part of the building process.

With the aid of the manufacturer's instructions, and the drawings and photographs contained in this article, you can enjoy a complete air conditioned home at a tremendous savings, and have the pleasure of knowing you did it yourself. •

INSTALLATION of a waterless conditioner in conjunction with an existing hot air heating system is shown here. The dealer is pointing to new ductwork. Cooler itself is set into basement window.

IN YOUR PRESENT HOME . . .

install a
window air conditioner

To cool a small area inexpensively, window units are just right.

INSTALLATION of window units takes little time, is quite simple, will save you as much as $20.

All photos in this story courtesy of Fedders Air Conditioning.

YOU can buy window air conditioners that will cool up to 800 square feet, and which can be plugged into ordinary 115-volt house current. Smaller ¾-hp units will cool up to 410 square feet. If you have 230 volts available, you can get a unit that will cool up to 1110 square feet.

Building construction, number of windows, number of room occupants, and how the sun strikes your house, all affect how much cooling a conditioner will give. Any qualified dealer can help you work out what your exact cooling load is and which is the best and most economical unit for your purposes.

Window units are easy to install, and installation kits are available for all sizes and styles of windows. Most conditioners are compact enough so that you can take them right home with you in the trunk of your car. This may save you a $5 delivery charge. A typical charge for installation is $20. You can easily save that, too. Study the installation techniques carefully before you begin, instead of trying to follow directions as you go along, and you'll find it goes faster and better. Professional installers take about a half hour to do a job like the one shown in the accompanying illustrations. You can reasonably count on its taking you not much over an hour.

Many dealers may try to offer you a $35 package arrangement on a window conditioner, the payment covering delivery, installation and a year's free service. Except in metropolitan areas, where a different policy is in effect, this is a method they use to pad the bill, for with all good makes of conditioners the year's free service is something you're entitled to *without any extra cost.*

At that, it's unlikely you'll need service. Service calls average only ½ call per year

FIRST STEP is to remove the unit's front panel. Although the unit shown here is the popular model made by Fedders, it's typical of most such units.

A LARGE UNIT will come bolted to wooden skids. First, remove the hexagon-head bolts and clamps which hold the chassis securely during shipping.

PULL THE CABINET free of its chassis and then remove the chassis from its skids. You may have to lift the chassis somewhat to slide it clear.

YOU MAY WANT to mount the unit flush with the inside or the outside of the window, or part way between. In any case, mark center point of sill.

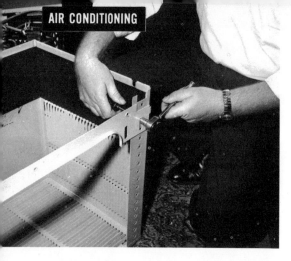

A TIE ANGLE is attached to the bottom of the cabinet. The position of the tie angle determines how far the unit will project into or out of room.

A SEALING ANGLE is attached to the top of the cabinet. Its position is determined by the amount of projection of unit. Pre-drill its screw holes.

IF OUTSIDE projection isn't very big, simple sill bracket will hold the unit. If projection is large, angle supports are needed for the job.

ANGLES are all adjustable, so that the cabinet may be made exactly level. When you're sure unit is perfectly level, tighten all nuts on supports.

per unit and most of these are for such elementary reasons as blown or loose fuses, unit not plugged in, or plug prongs bent so they aren't making good contact, and clogged air filters.

Installation does not include any changes in electrical wiring. Be sure your house voltage is within 10% of the voltage rating of the unit you buy. If you are in doubt about your house current, check with the power company or a local electrical contractor. The unit will probably come with a 6-foot cord. Any extension should be of heavy duty No. 14 wire at a minimum, and should not be over 25 feet long.

There is a decided advantage in buying an air conditioner that can also be reversed to give you heat. The unit then becomes something for year-'round use. Where mornings or evenings are cool and days hot, the unit will automatically switch from cooling to heating, as required to keep the temperature at the exact point you want. In most cases the added cost will be only about $20.

The best height at which to install an air

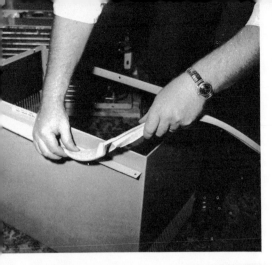

A RUBBER cabinet seal is pressed to fit onto the sealing angle. The ends of the rubber seal hook into slots arranged on ends of tie angle.

WITH THE CABINET in the window, and the sash pulled down to hold it, the tie angle is centered on the window sill and screwed or clamped to it.

MEASURE the window side-panels and then cut to size. The panels slide into slots in the sealing strip and also into fittings on window channels.

RAISE the window and slide the panels into the slots. Soap makes them slide easier. Then fit a piece of rubber sealer across tops of the panels.

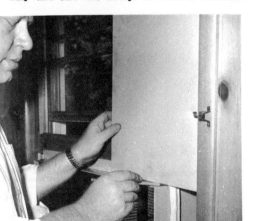

conditioner is about 30 inches, but this is not absolutely essential. Select a shady spot for it. If the sun is going to beat down on it, protect the unit with a ventilated awning. You'll get much better service.

You can get units that can be installed flush with the inside wall, flush with the outside wall, or balanced on the window sill at an intermediate point. In a flush inside mounting, allow enough of the unit to project into the room so the front panel can easily be removed, if required.

If your window sill is too narrow for

adequate support, use wood stripping to enlarge the sill's width. Check the level of the sill. For satisfactory operation, the unit must be exactly level. If it is off level, use thin pieces of wood to shim it up. The unit must be level both from front to back and from side to side.

For shipping purposes, the unit's compressor may be bolted down tight. If these nuts aren't loosened, noisy operation results. Usually, slide-out washers are placed under the nuts. Loosen the nuts only enough to remove these washers. •

Photo-Electric Burglar Alarm

Here's an excellent device for protecting your home against unwelcome visitors. It's especially useful in farm areas.

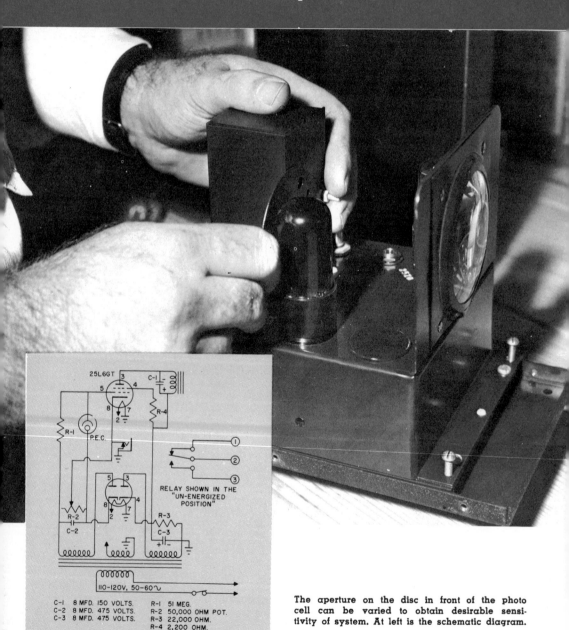

C-1   8 MFD. 150 VOLTS.
C-2   8 MFD. 475 VOLTS.
C-3   8 MFD. 475 VOLTS.

R-1   51 MEG.
R-2   50,000 OHM POT.
R-3   22,000 OHM.
R-4   2,200 OHM.

25L6GT

C-1

R-4

R-1   P.E.C.

RELAY SHOWN IN THE "UN-ENERGIZED POSITION"

R-2
C-2

R-3
C-3

110-120V, 50-60~

The aperture on the disc in front of the photo cell can be varied to obtain desirable sensitivity of system. At left is the schematic diagram.

Terminals on the case enable you to make all the necessary electrical connections to light source.

Careful adjustment of the bias control will increase usefulness of the unit. See photo above.

ORIGINALLY, we planned to include in this book a photo-electric system of our own design. As is common in such cases, we studied the available units on the open market, to see what design features were available. When we saw the Worner photo system, we stopped. Here was exactly what we planned to build, and many added features were included. For one thing, this unit comes in a completely weatherproof container and is fitted with pipe-mounting flanges for easier installation. A light shield is included to cut down on unwanted light and at a slight extra cost, mirrors are available which have adjusting screws for warping the mirror to a concave or convex form for focusing purposes.

There is nothing "magic" about photoelectric cells. We have devices that convert motion to sound (record player cartridges), that convert electricity to sound (loudspeakers), and electricity to light (electric lamps). Why not then, a device

that will convert light rays to electricity?

This is precisely what a photo electric cell does. When a concentrated light beam falls on the photo-sensitive surface of the cell, a small electric charge is generated which is amplified, and used to operate a relay, which in turn is used to switch the various controlled circuits on and off.

It is important, if the unit is to be operated at maximum efficiency, that the most intense light available be used. The Worner light source, designed for this purpose, is more than adequate, but you will have to lend your cooperation as well. You will have to be sure that the mirrors are not only focused to the ultimate point, but that all the components are properly aligned so that the most intense part of the light beam reaches the photo cell. The photo cell itself is designed to operate with even a minimum of light.

If you will follow the directions supplied with the unit, you should have ab-

View with rectifier tube removed shows the lens assembly. Large box is photo cell light shield.

Four screws at the bottom of each unit are provided to enable you to make leveling adjustments.

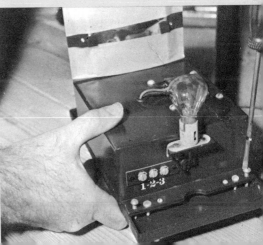

Follow instructions carefully when hooking up the unit. Below, external connections are made.

Part of kit is an alarm bell. Unit is housed in its own self-contained weatherproof container.

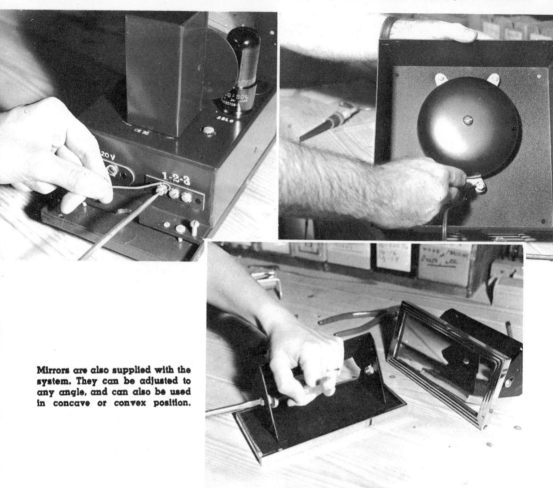

Mirrors are also supplied with the system. They can be adjusted to any angle, and can also be used in concave or convex position.

solutely no trouble. Just follow the instructions.

We formed a burglar alarm by surrounding our house with a light beam. We selected a rear corner of the house and mounted the light source box on one wall, the photo-cell on the other (see drawing). The two units point away from each other. At the three other corners we installed mirrors to reflect the light beam completely around the house from the light source to the photo cell. We then installed the control box outside the house, near the other units, and proceeded to follow the simple wiring instructions provided with the set.

We turn the system on every evening and thus far it has worked very well. Guests are surprised as they approach the door to hear the alarm, and it shakes the neighbors up as well. We have learned to shut the unit off when we expect guests and, fortunately, we have not as yet had any unexpected company in the form of burglars; but should they come, we are ready.

Naturally, any application where a switch is used to activate an electrical device can be operated by this system. You can use it as an effective garage door opener, alarm, or signal. Other applications are truly limited only by your own imagination.

The Worner Photo-Electric System, Rankin, Illinois, is available in various ranges, extending up to 5,000 feet. The lower range units are, of course, less expensive. •—*Byron G. Wels*

At right is bird's-eye view of a typical house, with mirror and photo cell installation. Below, the light source positioned at one corner of the house. Dark wrinkle finish of case makes it hard to see at night.

MIRROR NO. 3   LIGHT PATH   MIRROR NO. 2

CONTROL CENTER

LIGHT SOURCE

MIRROR NO. 1

PHOTO ELECTRIC CELL

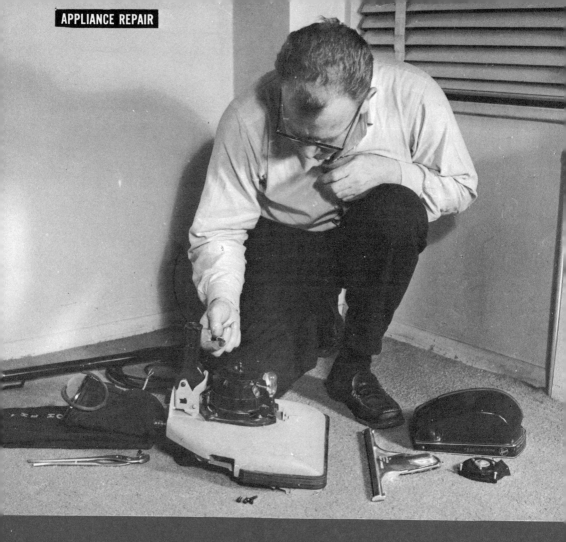

the ways and means
OF APPLIANCE REPAIR

T HE COMMONEST complaint about any appliance is that it doesn't work. Naturally, no self-respecting home handy man would get very far with such a complaint. He has to ask himself some questions. What doesn't work? How doesn't it work? Is it dead, or erratic, or noisy, or just unsatisfactory? Of course, any complaint about an appliance must be preceded by an assurance that it is being operated properly and within its capabilities. When we come to discuss specific appliances in following chapters, we'll discuss those complaints that are commonly caused by a failure to use the appliance the way it was meant to be used.

But right now, we're talking about real troubles, and one of the first things we'd ask ourselves is: "Is trouble electrical or mechanical?"

First, let's take electrical troubles, since they are the commonest. In checking for electrical troubles, it is convenient to imagine that electric current flows through wires like water through pipes, although a scientist might consider this very untechnical. Current flows, that is, when it is being used somewhere—to light a lamp, run a motor, heat an iron, etc.

The path traveled by electric current is called a "circuit," a term which implies a circle—which is a very apt description. Let's imagine a typical circuit. You know that your wall outlet has two holes, or slots. The plug that fits into it has two prongs. The cord connecting that plug to an appliance—let's say it's a light bulb—contains two wires. Now imagine that the current comes out of one of the two wires, goes through the filament of the bulb, and back in through the other wire. That would be a complete circuit. There is also a complete circuit on the inside of that wall outlet, leading back to the fuse box (or circuit breaker panel) and ultimately to the pole out on the street and all the way back to the generating station.

It's hard to imagine how electricity escapes from this complete circuit when there is no break in it, and there's no exact analogy for it. The closest thing to it would be a steam-heating system. The piping for such a system is a "closed circuit" from which the steam itself does not escape. It gives up its heat in the radiators, and this heat must be replenished to transform the returning water back into steam.

In a roughly comparable way, energy is taken out of your home's electrical system, even though the current travels around in a "complete" or "closed" circuit. Your electric meter records the amount of energy you use up, in kilowatt hours.

Electric current must have a complete circuit or else it won't flow. A switch, as on a lamp or an appliance, breaks the circuit when it is "off," makes it complete when it is "on." An incomplete circuit is called an "open" circuit, and no current flows in an open circuit. A switch is designed to open a circuit, but many "opens" occur accidentally—in which case the light or appliance affected will not operate. Open circuits are one of the three most common causes of electrical trouble which you will learn how to seek out and correct.

If a plug makes an imperfect connection in the wall, the result could be an open circuit. If the appliance cord has a break in one of the wires inside it, this would, of course, be an open circuit. When any wire becomes broken or disconnected, an open results and the circuit associated with it doesn't operate because no current flows in it.

The second common trouble is the "short circuit." A short circuit permits the current to travel a shorter path than it is meant to. Electricity always tries to follow the path of least resistance, just as water

ELECTRICAL MEASUREMENTS* OF SOME TYPICAL APPLIANCES

Typical Appliance	Voltage	Watts	Amperes	Resistance (in ohms)
Clock	115	2	.017	7,000
Shaver	115	10	.08	1,437
Portable Fan	115	50	.43	270
Ice cream freezer	115	100	.87	132
TV set	115	200	1.7	67
Food warmer	115	300	2.6	44
Automatic Washer	115	400	3.4	33
Casserole	115	500	4.3	27
Iron	115	1000	8.7	13
Ironer	115	1500	13.0	8.8
Range	230	2000	8.7	25.3
Clothes dryer	230	4500	19.0	12.1

*Approximate current, wattage and resistance relationships in electric appliances, especially heating appliances. This table is based on these formulas:

Watts = Volts × Amperes
Volts = Amperes × Ohms (resistance)
Ohms = Volts ÷ Amperes
Amperes = Watts ÷ Volts

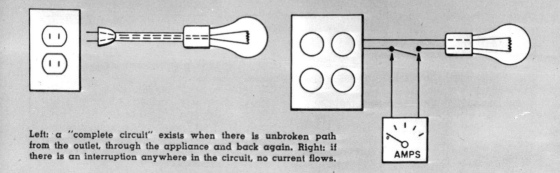

Left: a "complete circuit" exists when there is unbroken path from the outlet, through the appliance and back again. Right: if there is an interruption anywhere in the circuit, no current flows.

tries to run downhill. A short is a flood.

The wire in the heating element of a toaster or iron has a much higher resistance than the wires in the cord which connects the appliance to the wall. If these wires (in the cord) should touch each other—we would say they were "shorted" —the current would find an easier path to travel than struggling through the heating element. In other words, there would be a "short circuit."

When there is an open circuit, the appliance connected to it simply does not work. But a short circuit can blow a fuse because there is no resistance to limit the amount of current which can flow. In some cases, a short can cause a fire, when it is concealed and surrounded by combustible material.

Some shorts are accidental. An example is when wires are sloppily connected to screw terminals (perhaps in a plug) and some of the stranded ends from one wire touch the other one. A human being can create a short circuit by touching both wires at once (we call it touching "both sides of the line"). A person's ability to create a short circuit depends on the resistance of his skin. When the human skin is wet, its surface resistance is practically nil. The most notorious of this type of short circuit is the electric chair. Naturally, it will be an important part of this book to tell the reader how to repair appliances without the slightest risk of even mild shocks.

The third of the three most common types of electrical trouble is called a "ground." The earth, or ground, is the reference point for most electrical systems—that is, the point at which the voltage is zero. The ground, or "neutral" side of most home electrical systems is connected to the water pipes, since these go into the earth. Prop-

Left: "3-wire service" makes available either 120 or 240 volts. The "neutral" wire is grounded. Right: metal parts are grounded.

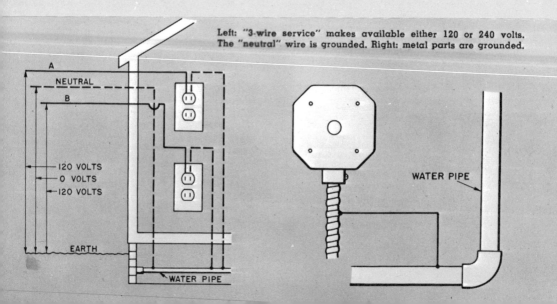

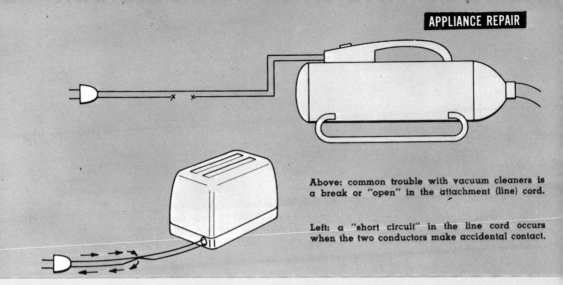

Above: common trouble with vacuum cleaners is a break or "open" in the attachment (line) cord.

Left: a "short circuit" in the line cord occurs when the two conductors make accidental contact.

erly, the connection should be made to point where the water system enters the house, since every joint between the electrical ground and the real earth may introduce resistance, and therefore an imperfect connection. There are three types of ground: "system ground," "equipment ground," and an unintentional or accidental ground.

The first of these refers to the grounding of the neutral conductor of the electrical system. The second refers to the grounding of the metallic shields, boxes, cases, etc., of all components of the electrical wiring system and any equipment which needs grounding. An accidental or unintentional ground occurs when one of the current-carrying conductors touches some metal it wasn't meant to touch, for example the metal case of an appliance. A ground of this type is a potential source of shock.

Let's see how this can happen. We know

that one side of the electrical system is connected to ground through the water pipe system. We'll suppose that the case of your electric mixer (often used near the kitchen sink) becomes grounded. Now all you have to do is touch the mixer and touch the water faucet and you've got a fairly complete circuit. And a shock.

If you were standing on the earth in damp shoes or bare feet, something similar could happen if you were using a portable electric saw or drill, or even an electric rotisserie. Appliances of this sort often have facilities for grounding the case, to eliminate the possibility of shock. Larger, high current appliances *always* do.

So far, we've established the fact that when something is wrong in an electrical appliance, it is usually caused by an open circuit, a short circuit or a ground. When a circuit is OK, it is "complete"; the flow of electric current has "continuity." If we

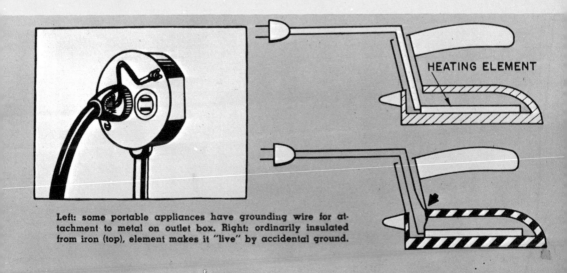

Left: some portable appliances have grounding wire for attachment to metal on outlet box. Right: ordinarily insulated from iron (top), element makes it "live" by accidental ground.

HEATING ELEMENT

Left: touching one prod of neon tester to cover screw of outlet proves that one side of the line is grounded.

Right: meter reads full line voltage (120) with one prod in outlet and one connected to metal outlet box cover.

Left: neon tester is safe, useful device to test for presence of voltage in outlets and on terminals in appliances. A small neon bulb lights up if the electric outlet is "live."

Right: test lamp has "pigtail" leads (connecting wires) for easy contact or insertion at the test points in appliance circuits and electric outlets.

Appliance testers such as shown here are extremely useful, versatile instruments providing more accurate indications than a test lamp.

Right: test lamp shown being used to see if outlet is OK. Pigtail leads are inserted in the outlet slots. This way is quick, satisfactory, portable.

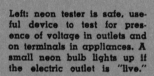
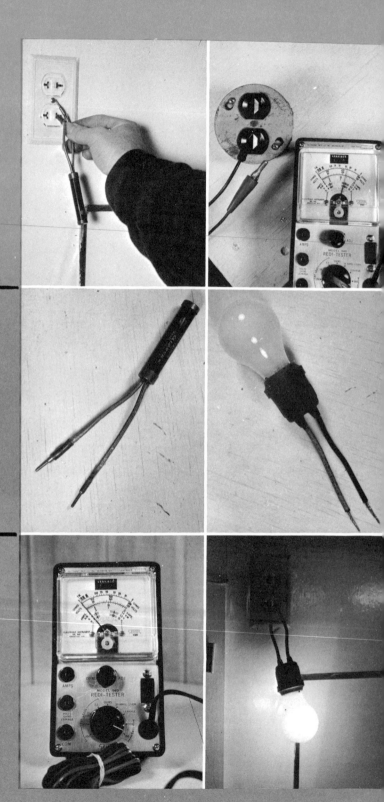

wish to test a circuit, we check it for continuity. In order to do this, we must pass some current through it and at the same time provide some visible indicator which will show us that the current did find its way all the way around the circuit—or, in other words, that the circuit has continuity. We consider the electrical circuit as commencing at an electrical outlet. The method we use for checking is to test segment by segment, so that we can isolate the trouble. Here's an example:

An electric lamp doesn't light. We test the bulb in another lamp and it works, so we know that's not the trouble. Step 1 is to test the outlet itself. If that's OK, step 2 is to check the cord: first, by visual inspection and second for electrical continuity. If the cord is OK, the only things left are the switch and the socket (which may be separate or all together). That's the general method—a step-by-step process of elimination.

Now how *do* we test or check for continuity? As we said above, an electric current is fed into the circuit and a visible indicator is used to determine whether the current has a successful trip. There are four commonly used indicators: (1) an ordinary light bulb, (2) a flashlight bulb, (3) a neon lamp and (4) a meter. The source of test current may be an ordinary electric outlet or a battery.

A bulb of any type which is used for this purpose is called a "test lamp." For testing on ordinary 110-volt house current, a regular light bulb is used in a socket with "pig-tail leads"—which is another way of saying that the wires (leads) for the socket are hanging out. This is a special type of socket, obtainable at an electrical supply store, which has no switch ("key-less"), is usually of molded rubber construction with the leads permanently attached. The leads are stiff, though flexible.

A neon tester serves the same purpose, is much smaller; it has the advantage of being more compact and the disadvantage of giving off a very small light which is not so easily seen. A continuity tester can be constructed with a flashlight battery and bulb, and the battery supplies the testing current (instead of a house outlet).

The word "meter" we used earlier is a loose term usually signifying some sort of test equipment which uses a meter as an indicator. The test equipment can tell us "how much," whereas the test lamp can only answer "yes" or "no" to the question of continuity. The Redi-Tester shown here can read voltage, current (amperes), resistance (ohms), power (watts) and leak-

age. Several different "scales" are printed on the face of the meter, for making these various measurements. Connections for the different measurements are made internally at the turn of a selector switch. The Tester illustrated was designed especially for do-it-yourself repair of home appliances.

When testing for continuity with a test lamp, we use the lamp to complete a circuit. If the circuit is otherwise continuous, the lamp will light. In other words, the lamp indicates that current is flowing through the circuit. Remember that if there were an open circuit, no current would flow and, therefore, the lamp would not light.

If we were using a test meter for testing, we would use it in the same way as the test lamp, by means of its test leads, and the needle on the meter would serve as the indicator. We will give an example in a moment to explain how to read it.

Using the regular house current for test purposes (with a test lamp or a neon tester) is called "dynamic" testing, since it tests the equipment under actual operating conditions. Using a battery-type continuity tester or a piece of test equipment for continuity checking is called "static" testing. Test equipment can also be used for dynamic testing.

We believe that static testing is preferable for the non-professional, because it is the safest. Of all the methods mentioned in the preceding paragraphs, dynamic testing with a test lamp is least preferred because it involves working with "live wires" at the risk of a shock. It is, however, a cheap method. The meter gives you the most information, is the most helpful and costs the most. We'll show all three methods here, so the reader can take his choice. But first a word about costs: The average home has at least twenty appliances, plus the lighting and wiring system. Over a period of two to five years, there will be many occasions to make your own repairs, which can save you quite a bit of money. In the long run, it's worthwhile to spend a few dollars to get the right tools and equipment to work with.

Now, let's go through the motions on a typical problem. We have an electric iron that doesn't work. It just doesn't get hot at all—no signs of life. We will go into more details about irons subsequently, but for the time being here's what they consist of: Outwardly, there's a piece of iron with a handle. Inside the piece of iron there's a heating element, which is simply a type of wire (it may be in a coil, a flat strip or

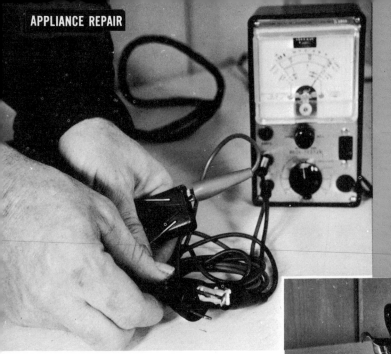

Either side of the line in an appliance cord can be tested for continuity with an ohmmeter as shown left.

Below: with iron cord in electric outlet, it is tested for continuity with a test lamp. Bulb lights, all OK.

Below: here's how a test lamp can be used to test for continuity in an appliance such as a flatiron.

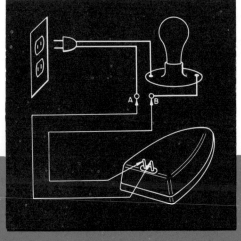

Below: iron cord is neither shorted (top test) nor open (bottom test). For bottom test, cord is shorted out with a screwdriver across plug.

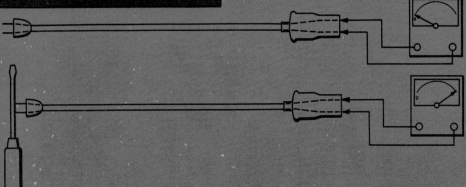

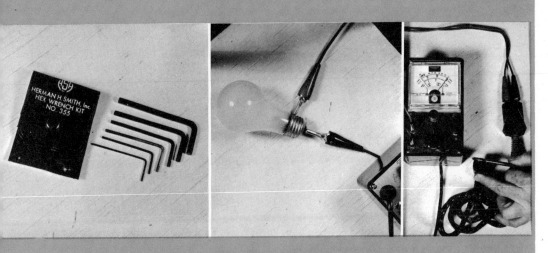

Left: set of Allen wrenches will find many uses, especially to remove set-screws from appliance controls. Center: light bulb is tested with an ohmmeter for continuity by contacting brass shell and tip on bottom. Right: testing cord for opens as shown in the drawing at the bottom of previous page. With plug shorted out by screwdriver, meter reads zero ohms, or a (normal) short circuit.

a rod) which covers most of the sole plate and which, because of its resistance to the passage of electric current, gets hot when current goes through it. There is a cord which connects the iron to an outlet. There is a plug on one end, that goes in the wall. On the iron end, there is usually another plug, which fits over a couple of prongs on the heel of the iron. In some cases, the cord is permanently attached to the iron. In one way or another, the cord connects to the heating element inside. But the connecting screws or prongs, as well as the heating element itself, are insulated from the body of the iron. There may also be an adjustment for the heat of the iron: this is a mechanical thermostat.

So, in essence, this gadget is simply a heating element, connected to an electrical outlet, and enclosed in an iron case which helps to hold and evenly distribute the heat and also give weight to the appliance. Now, since it doesn't work at all, we assume that no current is flowing through it. As we said earlier, no current will flow if there is an open circuit. Maybe that's the problem here.

To check it, we start with the source of the current—the wall outlet—and work outwards. Let's not *assume* that the wall outlet is OK; might as well check it. You can plug something else into it, such as a lamp. You can check it with a neon tester, which indicates the presence of voltage in the outlet. You can stick your test lamp into the outlet, if you have one. Or you can check it with a meter. A meter can

tell you *how much* voltage is at the outlet, which is sometimes useful, although in this instance it's not important.

Next, there is the cord. First, let's take a look at it. Not frayed or obviously broken anywhere? Good. Now, if it disconnects from the iron, we can check it by itself. If you're using a test lamp, you can plug the cord into the wall and touch the test lamp to the other end (one lead into each slot). It should light, of course. If you're using a battery-type continuity checker or a meter, you will bring both plug ends together, where they're handy to get at, and check each wire in the cord for continuity. You won't know at first which is which at each end of the cord. But once you've established continuity between one prong at one end and one at the other, you'll know that the other two should also show continuity. If you touch both prongs at one end, your checker should indicate no continuity. If it does indicate continuity, you know that the two conductors in the cord are shorted.

If you were using a meter, it would be an ohmmeter (to check resistance). An ohmmeter reads high ohms at the left and low (or zero) at the right. When the meter is at rest, the needle stands at the left, at the very highest point (infinity). If you short the prods together, the needle goes all the way to the right, or zero. When you put the prods on a short circuit, or a very low resistance path, the needle will swing over to zero, or so close to it you can't tell the difference.

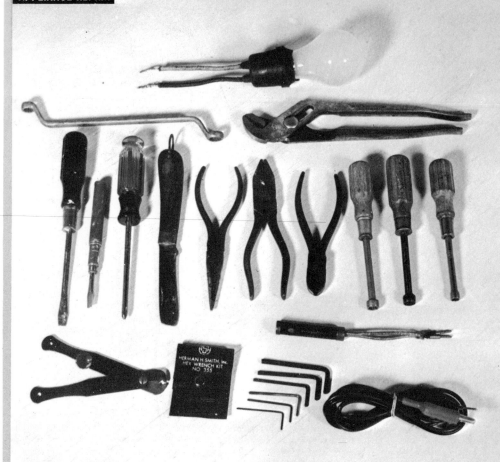

Useful aids to electrical servicing include screwdrivers, cutting pliers, wire strippers, nut-drivers.

Appliance repair centers in larger cities provide catalogs of replacement parts for most appliances.

Heating elements for appliances should be replaced as a unit rather than be patched or repaired.

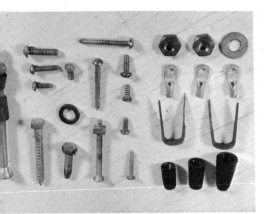

Above: assorted screws and connectors include wirenuts (bottom right), Romex staples just above.

Above: screw heads. Center is hex head, requiring nut-driver; 2nd from right is Phillips-head screw.

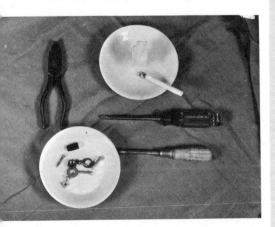

Keep screws and small parts together when disassembling appliance. They may be easily lost.

An appliance cord is a very low resistance circuit. Its resistance is a tiny fraction of an ohm, which wouldn't be readable on a meter, and the meter would read zero. So if you were using an ohmmeter for a continuity check, you would get a reading of zero if the wire were continuous. If the wire had an open in it somewhere, the needle wouldn't move (would stay at the highest point on the dial, namely at infinity).

There's a knack to using a meter which usually escapes the newcomer because he expects too much accuracy from it. If we are using a meter for an indication—as in the case of a continuity check—the needle is simply at one end or the other: left for open, right for short or continuous. If we are using a meter for an actual measurement—for instance, to check the resistance of a heating element—we are satisfied if the reading is within 10% of the expected value. Most ordinary test equipment isn't any more accurate than that and most equipment ratings aren't stated any more accurately by the manufacturer. If the heating element in a toaster should be 10 ohms, it's OK to get a reading of 9 ohms or 11 ohms (plus or minus 10%).

Now back to this iron which is on the fritz. We found that the wall outlet is OK and the cord and plugs are OK. So maybe there is something wrong with the iron itself.

The next step would be to check for continuity in the iron by checking across the prongs. With an ohmmeter or with a battery-type continuity checker, this is relatively simple, as shown here. With the type of test lamp we used earlier to test the wall outlet, it would not be possible. We can make up a rig incorporating a light bulb which can do the job, and this is illustrated here. If the "innards" of the iron are OK, the bulb will light.

Of course, in this hypothetical case we've just cited, the innards of the iron could *not* be OK. We've found everything else checks out and we know the iron doesn't work, so it must be the heating element inside. A check for continuity on that will reveal an open.

For the sake of argument, we'll say that this is an old-fashioned non-automatic iron, because we'll go into flatiron servicing more completely in a later chapter. As soon as we've located the trouble, the testing phase is ended and the troublesome part is repaired or replaced.

Replacement parts may be obtained from the authorized distributor of the appliance or from an appliance parts house. ●

safety measures

WHILE USING AND REPAIRING

MANY RULES, laws and codes exist to protect life and property from shock and fire due to electrical hazards. Some of these pertain to the manufacture of electric devices, equipment and appliances, while some pertain to the wiring of homes and commercial or public buildings.

Any homeowner with his wits about him could break a dozen rules without working up a sweat. And, most likely, no one would know about it—unless an "accident" happened. Then it might be too late.

No one would consider it very clever to circumvent a rule designed to protect him. And yet people are continuously doing it —through ignorance, thoughtlessness, being in a hurry, trying to save money, etc. The thousands of people who are killed and maimed every year in automobiles are sufficient proof of this.

We will try in this book to inform the reader about all necessary precautions, and to these we will add this one: "When in doubt, don't."

The first and most important rule is never to work on anything "live." If it's an appliance, disconnect it. If it's an electrical circuit, remove the fuse. This is a safety rule that will always stand you in good stead. Turning off a switch isn't enough—remember, that only disconnects one side of the line—if the switch works, that is.

If you work on the house electrical system, go one step further. Always check with a neon tester or a test lamp to make sure the circuit is dead *after* you remove the fuse. You might remove the wrong fuse once—and once is enough.

They say that "a little knowledge is a dangerous thing," and if it breeds over-confidence, it certainly is. No *good* workman ever disregards even the most basic safety precautions, and no amateur should, either.

Never touch an exposed "live" wire or connection with your hand or with anything else—as for instance, a screwdriver. There are many "accidents" that can happen this way. For instance, the moisture on your hand could make the wooden or plastic handle of a screwdriver a relatively good conductor. Or your finger might slip down onto the blade. Or the blade might slip and short out the two sides of the line. These are some of the reasons why rule No. 1 covers everything—always disconnect first.

You should know about "grounds" and "grounding." They can be beneficial and dangerous at the same time. Connecting the metal parts of an electrical system or an appliance to ground (through a water pipe) lessens the hazard of accidental shock. That's the beneficial side of the story. The accidental ground may lead to shock because—as we explained earlier—one side of the house wiring system is already connected to ground. If you were to accidentally touch one side of the line and at the same time be in contact with ground, you might be putting yourself directly "across the line."

This is the origin of the many old wives tales about people getting electrocuted while standing in a pool of water. The tales were true, but usually the people who tell them don't understand the real cause of the tragedy.

Let's say you're standing on the cellar floor. That's cement and it is in direct contact with the earth. If the cement were damp, its internal resistance would be lowered—or in other words, it would be a better conductor to ground. If you were standing on a wet spot, *you* would be making a better contact with the ground. That won't cause you any harm. Let's now suppose that you decide to change a light bulb or a fuse. That won't do you any harm, either. But if, in the process, you actually touch the metal shell forming the socket of the bulb or fuse, you are touching a current-carrying conductor (in other words, a "live" one). Now you've got your hand

First step in working on any house-wiring circuit is to completely remove the fuse that controls it.

You can find if an outlet is "live" with a neon tester, as shown, with a voltmeter, or test lamp.

GROUNDED MOTOR (3 WIRES) FOR SAFETY

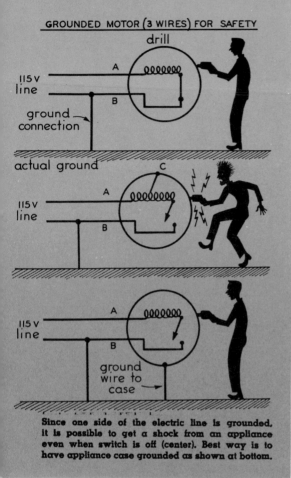

Since one side of the electric line is grounded, it is possible to get a shock from an appliance even when switch is off (center). Best way is to have appliance case grounded as shown at bottom.

on one side of the line and your feet are making a good, wet connection with the earth. Maybe you always wanted to be a live wire. . . .

We're not trying to scare you, but if we have, it's not a bad idea. It's good to have a healthy fear of electricity—enough fear to remember always to steer clear of live connections, and to turn things off whenever possible.

Electrical repair is one field where it really pays to be neat. Connections should be neat and clean, with no frayed ends sticking out to cause trouble. If you make connection to a screw terminal, no bare wire should stick out from under it. Always look over everything you've done when you finish with it to make sure you haven't created any new trouble or potential hazard.

Electrical connections should be secure, too, so that neither vibration nor an accidental pull will undo them. In addition, they should be protected from such accidental pulls.

That's the reason behind the famous "Underwriters' Knot" which almost everyone has learned at some time or other. This is a knot on the inside of an electrical plug which helps insure that if someone pulls on the cord, the strain will not be put on the electrical connections inside the plug. For this reason, it is called a "strain relief" knot. Strain relief knots are often found inside of lamps and fixtures, too, for the same reason. In electrical appliances, the cord—if permanently at-

You can prove one side of line is grounded. Here meter reads 110-volts with one lead on box cover.

Fuse should be removed before working on switch, shown here with cover plate off, terminals exposed.

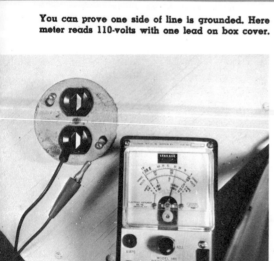

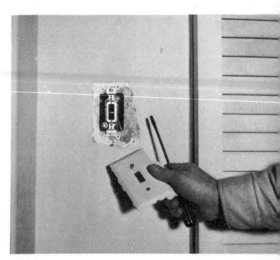

tached—is usually clamped in place, instead of being knotted.

Again for the same reason, nothing should ever be hung on a current-carrying electric cord. By that we mean, for instance, a chandelier or a hanging light fixture. The electrical connections, in other words, should not be carrying the weight of the fixture.

Care should be taken to avoid running wires across sharp edges which might eventually cut them; and also to avoid situations where movement and consequent friction might perform the same operation.

Of course, one should never put a nail or a staple through an electrical cord, since it might short out both conductors.

It would be handy, in discussing electrical precautions, if we were to get a little more exact about some of the terms we are using—particularly with reference to "wire." The average homeowner uses the word wire rather loosely to cover many things.

The stuff you ordinarily find on lamps, portable appliances and the like, to connect them to the wall outlet, is called "flexible cord," or simply, "cord." Sometimes we call it the "line cord." This cord usually contains two "conductors," which is the name of the current-carrying stuff inside—usually made of stranded copper wire.

It might interest you to know that the National Electrical Code (more about that in a moment) *prohibits* the following uses of cords:

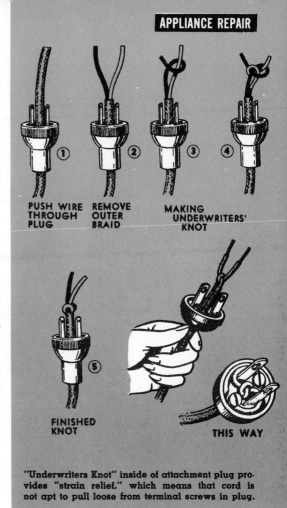

PUSH WIRE THROUGH PLUG — REMOVE OUTER BRAID — MAKING UNDERWRITERS' KNOT

FINISHED KNOT — THIS WAY

"Underwriters Knot" inside of attachment plug provides "strain relief," which means that cord is not apt to pull loose from terminal screws in plug.

Aids in wiring and appliance testing and repair are volt-ohm-ammeter, test leads and test lamp.

Fuse can be tested for continuity with ohmmeter when test prods are touched to shell and tip.

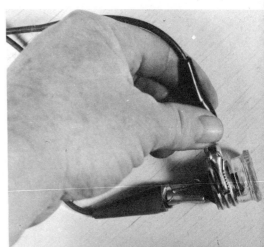

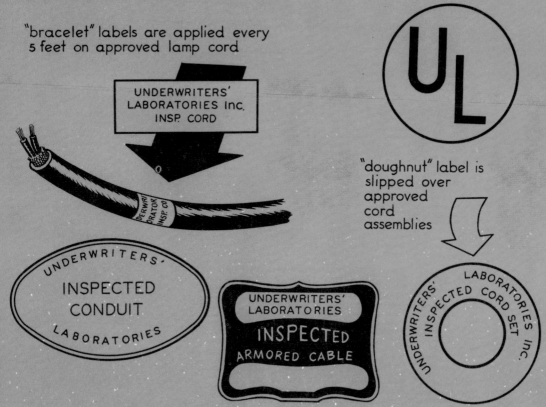

"bracelet" labels are applied every 5 feet on approved lamp cord

UNDERWRITERS' LABORATORIES Inc. INSP. CORD

"doughnut" label is slipped over approved cord assemblies

UNDERWRITERS' INSPECTED CONDUIT LABORATORIES

UNDERWRITERS' LABORATORIES INSPECTED ARMORED CABLE

UNDERWRITERS' LABORATORIES INSPECTED CORD SET Inc.

Various forms of "UL" label indicate that item is tested and meets specific underwriter standards.

1. As a substitute for the fixed wiring of a home.

2. Where run through holes in walls, ceilings or floors.

3. Where run through doorways, windows or similar openings.

4. Where attached to building surfaces, or

5. Where concealed within building walls, ceilings or floors.

Stop and think how many times you have used or seen a good old "extension cord" in one of these ways. They're proscribed because they're not safe. An extension cord is not—or should not be—a substitute for better wiring in the home. Oh, and here's another—cords should be continuous, not spliced.

The wiring of a home, the fixed wiring, uses "cable"—not "wires," nor "cord," but cable. There are two types in general use, mentioned earlier: armored cable (BX) and non-metallic sheathed cable (Romex). Sometimes—but usually not in homes—wiring is run through rigid metal conduit.

The conductors inside of these cables are solid, rather than stranded, because they are not designed for continuous flex-ing. While most cords contain No. 18 gauge conductors, the smallest conductors used in cables are No. 14—which is specified as a minimum for 15-ampere circuits.

The National Electrical Code specifies the minimum size conductors for all circuits, based on the amperage. A table of such sizes was given in an earlier chapter. These sizes are chosen in proportion to the amount of heat which will be generated in them when the maximum amperage named in the rating passes through them.

Never replace any cord or cable with something smaller than you found. As a safety precaution, this is just the opposite of the rule on fuses—which is, never replace a fuse with one of a higher rating. A fuse is like a burglar alarm—it lets you know when there is trouble in the house. Putting in a larger fuse is like turning the burglar alarm off: it leaves you without any protection.

The guiding standard for most electrical work is a document known as the "National Electrical Code." This is not a federal law but rather a private standard which "represents the consensus of a highly qualified body of experts—it is generally recognized

Antiquated fuse arrangement is likely candidate for inadequate wiring, has too few branch circuits.

Heating elements of toaster are exposed, should never be touched while toaster is plugged in.

as having an exceedingly high value to the public and to the electrical industry."

The electrical code is the standard of the National Board of Fire Underwriters, as recommended by the National Fire Protection Association. This association is one of fire insurance companies.

The Code is not a national law, but it may be adopted—in whole or in part or with modifications—as a local law. The provisions of the Code are so widely accepted that they may just as well be considered as law.

Underwriters' Laboratories, Inc., is an organization which formulates standards for manufactured materials for electrical use, consistent with National Code requirements; tests manufactured materials (at the request of the manufacturer) for conformance with these minimum standards; and certifies those materials which conform.

The famous "UL" label—signifying that a product has been inspected and approved by the Underwriters' Laboratories—is a hallmark not easily come by (for manufacturers) and one to be sought after by the consumer on products he buys. •

HOW TO REPAIR
fans and mixers

FANS ARE one of the simplest types of motor-driven appliances. The common portable or table fan consists of a motor with the fan blades directly connected to the motor shaft. An on-off switch may be provided, and sometimes a 2- or 3-speed switch. Usually these smaller fans have no brushes or internal switches or capacitors and have little that can go wrong with them. The bearings are usually packed with grease that will last the life of the fan. A simple oscillating mechanism is sometimes supplied.

Some fans of this size, in order to be suitable for A.C. and D.C. operation, have universal motors, which are subject to the usual brush and commutator troubles outlined in the chapter on motors.

Larger fans, such as pedestal fans, will have split-phase or capacitor-start motors and some—such as attic fans—have a belt connection between the motor and the fan blades.

The only load on a fan is the resistance of the air to its blades, and this does not change. A possible exception might be a fan which was placed so as to work against a strong wind. This, of course, is an illogical situation. An attic ventilating fan, for instance, should be positioned so as to work with the prevailing breeze (when there is one). Otherwise it can't do any good.

The mission of a fan is to move air—to assist in circulation, or to move hot air out so that cool air will come in and take its place. The capacity of a fan is usually expressed in cubic feet of air per minute, and is determined largely by the length of the

Westinghouse

The capacity of a fan is usually expressed in cubic feet of air movement per minute. This will depend on the length, pitch and speed of the blades, and determine what size of motor will be required.

Emerson

blades, the pitch of the blades and the speed of the blades. Naturally, the more air the blades are capable of moving, the more power is required from the motor—or rather, the more powerful a motor is needed.

Some complaints are registered against fans when the trouble is merely that they are not suited to the task. This is true of many kitchen exhaust fans, which fail miserably when something being fried gives off a lot of smoke.

The commonest legitimate complaints about fans are: (1) Won't run, (2) Runs slow and (3) Runs noisy.

If the fan will not run, we first want to know if it's getting current, or in other words, if it provides a complete or continuous circuit from the wall plug outlet. A test-lamp or a test meter applied to the prongs of the plug should show continuity when the switch (if there is one) is turned

on; and if it is a 2- or a 3-way switch, there should be continuity in every position except "off."

When continuity is not discovered this way, a point-by-point check is necessary, to test the cord, the switch, and the connection of the switch to the motor. Usually the trouble will be discovered in this process. If not, then testing of the motor in the various ways mentioned in the chapter on motors will be necessary.

A fan that runs slow may have one of the motor troubles outlined in the previous chapter or it may have a defective speed control.

A fan which is noisy can have one of several types of mechanical troubles outside of the motor itself. The commonest of these are loose parts, especially in the safety guard over the blades, or bent blades. The latter can cause much more trouble than the insignificance of the

If fan won't run, first test for continuity by applying test meter to the prongs of the plug.

In order to remove a defective switch, first remove the lock nut from the outside of the fan.

To disassemble the fan, it must be disconnected from the oscillating mechanism as is shown here.

End cap must be removed for point-by-point check of the cord, switch and connection to the motor.

trouble would indicate. If, through handling or accidentally hitting the blades, they become bent, then their symmetry is destroyed. This lack of symmetry will cause the whole body of the fan to vibrate and rattle. It may also affect the speed of the fan. To check this, select some point of reference on the cage or guard and measure with a ruler to some easily identifiable point on a blade. Then slowly move the blades around and check each one in the same place. Restoring symmetry to

the blades can effect an amazing improvement in quietness and steadiness of the fan.

Food mixers, like fans, are simple motor-driven appliances. But they have these differences: they always have speed control, they have a gear-train to drive the beaters and they have a variable load. That is, there is a decided difference between mixing powdered milk and mixing a cake batter, as far as the resistance to the beaters is concerned.

Food mixers experience most common trouble in the flexible cord, the switch and speed control.

To disassemble, remove brushes and speed control knob. Take case apart by removing long screws.

Here, the motor and armature are exposed; connection to the speed control may now be checked.

Remove armature to clean commutator. Brushes are here placed in respect to commutator as in motor.

Mixers all have universal motors, which means they are subject to brush trouble. The commonest troubles, however, are in the flexible cord, the switch and the speed control. Very little trouble is ever experienced with the gears, which are usually permanently packed in grease. It is conceivable, however, that a tooth might be sheared off if the beaters hit something solid. The symptom of a "stripped" gear would be that the motor runs but the beaters do not.

Common troubles with mixers include opens in the flexible cord, the switch or the speed change circuits and lack of lubrication in the bearings. Motor troubles typical of universal motors and described in the previous chapter may be encountered.

Disassembly of a typical mixer (Dormeyer) is illustrated here. This unit is characterized by a tapped field winding type of speed control and a vertically mounted motor. Horizontally mounted motors require a worm gear arrangement in order to transfer power to the vertically mounted beaters.

Brushes may be removed for inspection from the mixer shown without disassembling the machine. A dirty commutator, however, could not be reached without disassembly.

Before the motor can be disassembled, the speed control knob and the brushes must be removed. The second step is typical of many motors, in that long screws which hold the upper housing to the field and switch assembly are removed. This exposes the motor, and the armature may be extracted for inspection of the commutator. Connections to the speed control are also exposed, and resistance or continuity checks may be made on the various windings. To expose the gears, it is necessary to unscrew the field-and-switch-assembly from the bottom, or gear, housing. It is advisable to do this carefully so that the gears will not be disturbed, as there may be nothing wrong with them. With the motor shaft removed, there is nothing to hold the gears in place except the grease in which they are packed. Wiring from the speed control to the fields should not be disturbed unless a fault is discovered in that area. If the wires are disturbed, they should be tagged so that they can be put back the way they were.

Reassembly would proceed in the reverse of the above procedure. After the gear housing was reattached, the motor shaft would be inserted into the gears and gently turned until it falls into place. When the upper housing is replaced, care should be taken not to squeeze any wires between the housing and the motor; and at the same time, to place them as they were originally so that they will not get in the way of moving parts. Then the brushes, if they are OK, will be replaced. Ideally, they would have been numbered when removed, so that each could be put in the same slot. If new brushes are installed, they must be formed to the curvature of the commutator. The best way to do this is to put a piece of sandpaper between the brush and the commutator and slide it back and forth so that the curvature of the commutator is worked into the brush. Last to go back is the speed control knob.

When disassembling any motor care should be taken not to drop or misplace any shims which might fall out from their position at the ends of the shaft, for they determine the proper end play of the shaft. Usually these are very thin fiber washers which stick in the bearing because of the lubricant, and then drop out if the housing is roughly laid down.

The Waring Blendor is a common household appliance which is similar in its principle of operation to a food mixer, although its manner of assembly and its end purpose are different.

Here the turning power of the motor is coupled to a set of blades in the bottom of the glass Blendor. Coupling is not permanent, and is made positive by the holding action of four rubber clamps into which the glass fits. A simple universal motor is used, usually with a 2-speed control utilizing a tapped field.

Troubles in the Blendor are similar to a mixer—won't run, runs noisily, won't come up to speed, or motor runs but blades do not. This, however, is a direct drive machine, so the latter trouble would not be due to gears but rather to improper seating of the glass Blendor jar. In general, solution of troubles is exactly the same as with the food mixer.

Nothing can be inspected in this machine, however, without complete removal of the outside housings. At first glance, this defies the ingenuity of the home handy man. It is relatively easy, however. Starting at the top, after the glass is lifted off, we see a square stud sticking up, which engages the blade mechanism in the bottom of the glass. This stud can be turned with a wrench and it will come out. Then a small cover plate lifts off, revealing a large hex nut. A rather large open-end wrench can be used, if available, but the water-pump pliers worked admirably.

A similar large hex nut on the bottom of the unit allows the bottom housing to be removed, exposing the whole mechanism, which is protected by a specially fitted piece of Kraft paper. Do not tear this paper in removal.

The brushes may now be removed for inspection. If it is desired to get at the commutator, the upper half of the motor frame may be unbolted, via long screws which go through the field and which have nuts on the bottom. The commutator is now exposed for inspection and cleaning if necessary.

In reassembly, nut drivers will be found most helpful in putting back the main motor bolts, as it is hard (if not impossible) to hold the nuts in place otherwise. The Kraft paper protective cover is then replaced and the upper and lower housings reassembled. Care must be taken to dress the wires to the switch so that they do not interfere with reassembly and are clear of moving parts. •

The Waring Blendor is similar in its operation to a food mixer, although its assembly differs.

After lifting off the glass, a hex nut is removed from the bottom to release the lower housing.

Shown is the lower housing removed. Note that the line cord slips through the hole in housing.

Below the small cover plate, hex nut is revealed which holds upper housing. Here, both removed.

You can now see the specially fitted Kraft paper around the motor. Brushes may now be removed.

Here the Kraft paper has been removed. The motor frame may be unbolted to get at the commutator.

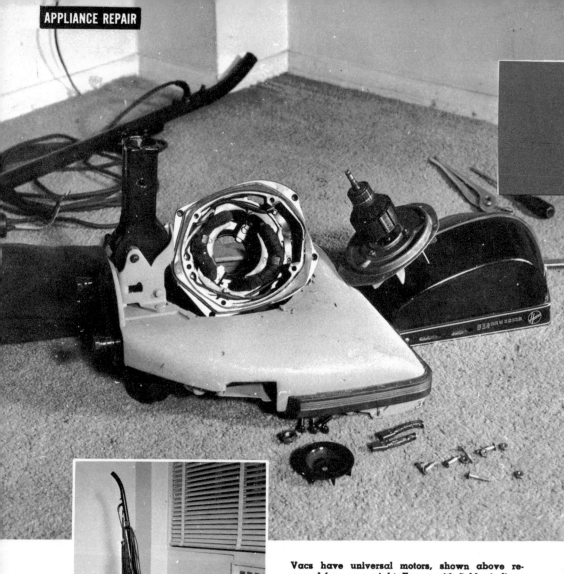

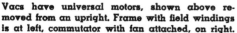

Vacs have universal motors, shown above removed from an upright. Frame with field windings is at left, commutator with fan attached, on right.

Uprights have external bag or separator, and a motor-driven brush which helps loosen embedded dirt from carpets and rugs. Shown is a Hoover.

Tank and canister cleaners are more mobile, have high power, are best for smooth surface floors and above-floor cleaning, lack moving brush.

THE INSIDE STORY ON
vacuum cleaners

ONE OF the most common home appliances in use, the vacuum cleaner is essentially a motor—a universal motor—with a fan on one end. One of the laws of physics is that "every action has an equal and opposite reaction." The motor-driven fan of the vacuum cleaner creates a high air pressure. The "equal and opposite reaction" is that a low pressure, or a partial vacuum, is created at the opposite end of the machine. Another law of physics is that "nature abhors a vacuum." This means that air rushes in and tries to fill the vacuum. The result is an apparent suction at the low pressure end of the cleaner. Anything in the way—such as surface dirt on a carpet—gets sucked in with the air.

An understanding of that principle is essential to an understanding of the operation of a vacuum cleaner. The flow of air must be continuous and relatively unimpeded. On an upright vacuum cleaner, for instance, the bag is porous. A flow of air through the bag is essential to the operation of the cleaner. If you put your nose near the bag of an upright, you can smell the dust coming through it. This is a normal situation, demonstrating the fact that the bag is porous and that air flows through it. Of course, most of the dust and soil remains inside the bag.

The principle of the "tank" type cleaner and the various variations of it is identical. In the typical tank cleaner, there is still a porous bag which allows the continuous flow of air. But usually this bag is concealed inside the cleaner.

The upright cleaner employs a motor-driven brush to agitate the nap of a rug or carpet, which helps to loosen embedded dirt in the pile and allow it to be sucked up into the bag. This brush also aids in picking up threads, lint, dog hairs, etc. To accommodate this brush, the area of the nozzle in contact with the rug must be fairly large, which limits amount of effective suction available in this type.

Tank and canister type cleaners are "straight suction" types. That is, they rely on suction alone, without the motor-driven brush. The area of the nozzle in contact with the rug can be smaller and therefore the effective suction is greater. Brushes and combs have been built into these nozzles to aid in picking up threads, hairs, etc.

In spite of improvements in the nozzle, the tank cleaner has always been inferior to the upright in cleaning carpets. To overcome the lack of a motor-driven brush, the manufacturers have stepped up the power of the motor till many of the late model cleaners have a suction as much as 4 times that of an upright. They will pick up almost anything. Nevertheless, a family with a good deal of wall-to-wall carpeting can do a better carpet-cleaning job with the upright, motor-driven brush type of cleaner.

The tank cleaner has other advantages, however, which maintain its popularity. These are its easier mobility in use; the facility for going under and behind things, like furniture and radiators; its superiority on hard-surface floor coverings which have been gaining so in popularity, such as linoleum, asphalt tile, rubber tile, etc.; and finally its facilities for above-the-floor cleaning of such as walls, moldings, window-sills, furniture, etc. Generally, also, the tank or canister cleaner is easier to store when not in use, and easier to carry from place to place in the house.

In the tank cleaner, the bag is located at the intake end of the machine. The dirt-laden air sucked up through the nozzle and the hose passes through the bag, where most of the dirt is separated from the air. The air then passes through the motor and out the other end, where there is usually an additional dust filter to clean the air before it re-enters the room. The canister cleaner operates in a similar way, except that the motor is in an upright position.

Top left: removing end-cover of tank vac; Right: the motor is exposed and one brush removed; Bottom left: underneath view of switch, showing solder connections; Bottom right: with switch "off," ohmmeter reading is "infinity"; Far right: with switch "on," the meter shows continuity.

Air is sucked in at the bottom and exhausted at the top. Various substitutes for a bag are employed in the canister cleaner, to separate the dirt from the air, such as cloth filters and water.

On the upright cleaner, the moving air flows past but not through the motor on its way from the nozzle to the bag. The bag, of course, is exposed. Uprights run on wheels, and an adjustment of nozzle height permits an adaptation to the type of carpet —deep pile or smooth pile. The nozzle brush is powered by a belt connected to motor. Usually there is a light on the front to help see the floor and especially see under things.

Since the tank cleaner depends on a high velocity of air movement, anything which impedes this flow will reduce the suction. This could include such things as: clogged nozzle, obstruction in the hose, very full bag, old bag which has lost much of its porosity, and dirt-laden filter. A poor connection of any of the fittings—such as nozzle to pipe sections and/or to hose and hose to cleaner—will cause a loss of suction

at the nozzle, where it is needed. A tiny hole or tear in the hose will also cause lost suction.

These faults (obstructions and air leaks) should be carefully checked when the complaint is that the cleaner won't pick up. Air leaks can be detected by holding the ear close to the various parts concerned, where the whistle of entering air will be heard if the fitting is not secure.

The path of air in the upright is more direct, and the only likely source of air leak is at the attachment of the bag to the exhaust port. An over-full bag, of course, will impede the passage of air out through the bag and cut down suction. An old, dirt-laden bag in an upright can also lose its porosity and impede the passage of air. A special problem of the upright is that the belt may break or lose its tension, causing absence of the revolving brush action. Or the nozzle may be improperly positioned (in height) with relation to the carpet.

The two principal complaints about cleaners are that they won't run at all, or

they run but don't clean properly. We have discussed some of the reasons why the cleaning action may be inadequate:

Tank cleaner	Upright cleaner
1. Clogged nozzle	1. Clogged nozzle
2. Obstruction in hose	2. Brush needs cleaning
3. Full bag	3. Obstruction to the bag
4. Old bag	4. Old bag
5. Old filter	5. Broken belt
6. Air leaks at connections	6. Belt is weak, loose
7. Air leak in hose	7. Belt is on backward
8. Motor runs slow	8. Nozzle at wrong height
	9. Motor runs slow

The motor may run slow due to a fault in the motor itself or due to an imperfect air path. You can demonstrate this to yourself by removing the bag from either a tank or an upright cleaner. The motor will run faster. It follows that a very full bag, for instance, would increase the load on the motor and cause it to labor. A large obstruction in the hose of a tank cleaner will also have this effect. Too tight a belt on an upright can also slow down the motor.

Internal causes of the motor running slow would include these: dirty or pitted commutator; worn or imperfectly seated brushes; partially shorted field winding; and low line voltage due to inadequate and/or overloaded house wiring.

If the cleaner doesn't run at all, testing for electrical continuity and for motor faults follows patterns previously mentioned. The commonest trouble in a vacuum cleaner is in the attachment cord and plug. These get a lot of use and abuse in normal use, and a break or an open circuit is common. The switch, too, will break down eventually from constant use. The entire electrical path can be checked at once by using a continuity tester or a meter at the plug prongs. When the switch is turned on, continuity should exist, and when it is turned off, an open circuit is indicated. Proper indications give a clean bill of health to the whole system.

If, however, no continuity is revealed in either position of the switch, the system must be subjected to a point-by-point test: the plug, the cord, the attachment of the

Height of motor-driven brush can be adjusted for different pile depths by height of rear wheels.

Continuity of cord, through the switch and the handle, can be checked as shown with test lamp.

The unit motor and fan assembly can easily be removed from an upright vac to clean commutator.

Commutator is the small part, here on left end of armature, on which the brushes make contact.

cord to the machine, the switch itself, and the connections to the motor. Usually the trouble is in the cord, with the switch coming in second place.

The upright cleaner has a few additional parts in this path. The cord attaches to the handle, where the switch is located. Then it runs down through the handle and makes connection to the cleaner. It is not likely that a break would occur in the conductors inside the handle, but trouble is possible in the attachment of the cord to the handle, in the switch, and in the attachment of the handle to the cleaner.

Blackened contacts at any make-and-break connection indicates arcing, which is a sign of a loose or poor connection.

If the electrical path is complete to the motor, the brushes should be checked for contact on the commutator. They may be

worn down to a nub, or they may be jammed in their holders.

Motor brushes work something like the flint in a cigarette lighter. There is a spring which maintains pressure of the flint against the wheel which causes it to spark. When the flint gets too short, the spring can no longer exert sufficient pressure. Sometimes, too, the spring loses its tension with age. This is less apt to happen in a motor, where the spring is not removed as often as it is in a lighter. In a lighter, you will also notice that the end of the flint becomes rounded from abrasion by the starting wheel. Motor brushes also get rounded from contact to the commutator. This is proper, for only by being so shaped can they make full contact with the commutator.

If the trouble is not in the brushes, it

Below, two canister types, the Lewyt and Airway, work on same general principles as tank cleaners.

Below, diagrams show connection of radio-interference condensers. Text describes test methods.

spection of the commutator is not. On this motor, the fan assembly is permanently attached to the armature shaft.

The ohmmeter reading for continuity across the line plug of this unit was 10 ohms, a typical value for a machine of this size. With a meter or a continuity tester, you can demonstrate to yourself the series circuit arrangement of the universal motor by removing a brush from its holder. Now testing across the line will show an open circuit. This shows you what would happen if a brush were not making contact with the commutator.

An upright cleaner may run slowly and be hard to push across the floor if the nozzle is too close to the carpet. This can easily be checked by rocking the cleaner back so that the nozzle is temporarily raised. If the trouble is revealed, a permanent nozzle-height adjustment is made.

It is common practice on newer cleaners to provide a condenser to suppress radio interference noise from the motor. This is a much smaller condenser than that found on capacitor-start motors. Typical practice is to put a condenser across the (AC) line. Sometimes an additional condenser is connected to ground (the metal case of the cleaner), or a 2- or 3-section condenser is used, combining these functions. If a condenser or one section of it is shorted, one of two things may result: the line may be shorted out, which would probably blow a fuse, or the line may be grounded to the case, with resultant shock hazard. Testing of condensers was described in a previous chapter. A shorted condenser is easy to spot, since it displays continuity in test. ●

would be in the armature or field windings. If checks firmed down to these points, the motor would either have to be replaced or taken to a service shop for repair.

Partial disassembly of a tank cleaner is illustrated. With the brushes and commutator exposed, these can be inspected. The color and condition of the commutator, as explained earlier, is an indicator of, and a possible source of trouble. If it is blackened, arcing at the brushes is a likely cause. Imperfect seating of the brushes can cause this. The armature can be cleaned with a piece of fine sandpaper while the motor is running. The brushes would be replaced, of course.

A more complete disassembly of a Hoover upright cleaner is also shown. The brushes can be removed from this machine without removal of the motor, but a careful in-

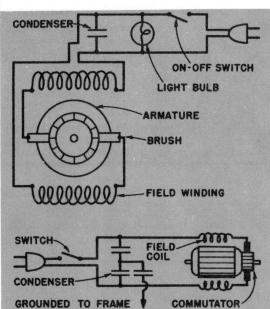

INSTALLING AND FIXING
dishwashers

Proper racking of dishes and silver in an automatic dishwasher is necessary, not only for satisfactory cleaning of load but also to avoid breakage.

THE PRINCIPAL TYPES of dishwashers which will be referred to here are: the portable; the free-standing but plumbed in type; the under-counter "built-in," and the combination dishwasher-sink. In general, the principles of operation and resultant servicing problems are similar in these types except that the portable requires water and electrical connections to be made before each use. The presence of a flexible attachment cord with this type introduces the possibility of opens in the cord and poor connection at the outlet, not present with the other types.

Almost all dishwashers wash by means of a strong spray of hot water coming up from the bottom. It hits the dishes from the bottom directly and from the sides and top indirectly by bouncing off the inside of the tub. Because of the force of the spray, all dishwashers turn off when the lid is lifted or the door or well is opened.

The most common source of energy for the spray is an impeller (vane) in the bottom, which is rotated by direct connection to the motor shaft. Some machines have a revolving arm in the bottom with jets (perforations) from which the water emerges. A few machines wash from the top down.

An electric motor, of course, is an important component of the dishwasher;

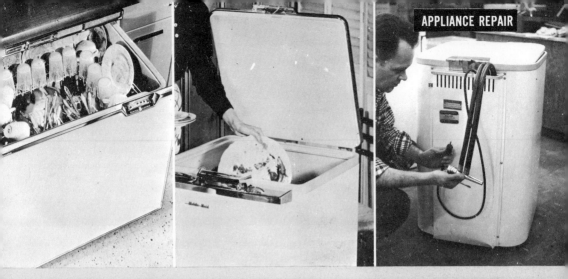

Above left: pull-out drawer is one of three basic types of loading. Whether drawer, drop-down shelf as on previous page or top-loading (center), a switch is provided to shut off water when opened. Portable unit (center) may be loaded at the table, requires water and electrical connections (right).

other components include a timer and water valves. A supply of hot water is presumed. Some models have a supplementary water heater and thermostat as well as facilities for heat-drying. Some have gravity drain, while others have a pump to drain the water.

Motor servicing is described in a previous chapter. There is a good deal of similarity in some of the other parts—such as timer, valves, pump—to washing machines described in the next chapter.

Here is a typical cycle of operation for pump-drain type with heat for drying: the washing time is 20 minutes, the drying time 30 minutes, for a total of 50 minutes. The washing cycle is commenced with a 45-second spray and drain, to rinse the dishes. This is followed by a wash (with detergent) for approximately five minutes, after which there is a 45-second drain, and then another five-minute wash. This is followed by a 45-second drain, a 1½-minute rinse, another drain and another rinse and another drain. Then comes about 20 minutes of drying with electric heat with the impeller on and a final drying of about 10 minutes with it off.

These various operations are triggered off by the timer, in which a synchronous motor drives a set of cams which turn switches on and off as the timer motor turns. There are five cams, to control: (1) The timer motor, which is always on when the machine is on, (2) the impeller motor, which is on during all except the last 10 minutes, (3) the heating element, which is on during the last 30 minutes, (4) the water inlet valve and (5) the drain

pump and drain valve. This is the "brain."

The two motors and the heating element are simply turned on and off by switches operated by the cams. The pump is also so operated, but the inlet and drain valves are controlled by solenoids (for all practical purposes, this is an electro-magnet) which are energized by switches in the timer.

If the washer does not run and if the electric supply checks OK up to the timer and if the door or lid switch is OK, listen to see if the timer is running (it hums). If so, the individual components will have to be checked for electrical continuity and for presence of electricity when it is called for. If the impeller motor does not run but the impeller turns freely by hand, check for voltage to the motor. It should be energized as soon as the washer is turned on. If it is getting voltage, check the motor. If it is not, the fault is in the timer or the wiring harness.

If water does not enter and if voltage is reaching the inlet valve solenoid (and, of course, the water is turned on), check for a stuck valve or stuck solenoid or an open in the solenoid. If the water doesn't drain, check for voltage to the drain valve solenoid, or for stuck valve or stuck solenoid, clogged drain or (if present) defective pump—stuck, clogged, etc.

Satisfactory washing requires that the dishes and silver be prepared and loaded as explained in the Owner's Manual. This means that dishes are scraped and rinsed under the faucet and loaded in the washer to get maximum washing efficiency plus maximum capacity load, combined with

Automatic soap (detergent) dispenser is provided on some models, seen here at top of drawer.

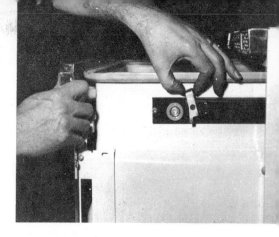

To completely remove drawer for servicing, roller slide is disengaged by lifting up the wheel stop.

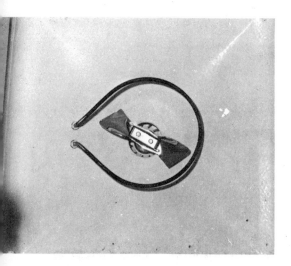

Impeller throws water up and around dishes. Circular tube is heating element for water, drying.

Washer is laid on side to show underneath placement of impeller motor, drain pipe, connections.

safety to the dishes. Also required is an adequate supply of hot water as well as adequate wiring to insure operating voltage for the motor.

If the dishes are not stacked properly, they may not only get unsatisfactory cleaning, but also may be thrown around and broken. On those machines which do not have a protective screen for the impeller, a common trouble is broken dishes or large food particles (such as bones) wedged in the impeller. Since the impeller is directly connected to the motor, the motor will not run if the impeller is jammed. That is why one of the first checks is to see if the impeller will turn freely by hand. If this should happen, check the fuse after the impeller has been cleared, as it may

have blown when the motor was locked.

The incorrect type or quantity of detergent will adversely affect cleaning action of the dishwasher. Manufacturers recommend special dishwasher detergents, which are usually low-sudsing and very strong.

All major appliances should be properly grounded to avoid shocks. On the portable dishwashers, this is usually accomplished through the attachment cord, designed for use with grounded outlet boxes. If the outlet boxes in your home are not grounded, special provision will need to be made for grounding.

In time, the door gasket will dry up and become brittle and require replacement. This, plus the jammed impeller, are the most common troubles encountered. •

HOW TO USE
AND REPAIR
washing machines

The basic principles of operation and common causes of trouble in the two main types: Agitator and Cylinder.

ABOUT EIGHT OUT OF TEN homes today have some sort of clothes washing machine, and it goes without saying that a great many types and brands are represented among these many millions of machines. It would not be possible in a book of this size to cover every one of these types and brands in full detail, so we have worked out the following plan to provide the reader with maximum coverage of useful information. A number of the most popular types and brands are completely covered; in addition, in the next few pages, we will cover the main, underlying principles and the common components of all types. If it should happen that your washer is not one of those which is covered in detail, you will nevertheless be able to service it with the information provided. By studying the information on the model which is most similar to yours, plus the general information in these introductory pages and in the Trouble-shooting Table, you will find it relatively easy to adapt this information to your washer.

Practically all automatic washers are one of two types: agitator or tumbler. The agitator-type is loaded from the top and has a post or vane in the center of its tub. This vane agitates the clothes to help the soapy water penetrate and loosen up the dirt. The generic term for the vane is "agitator," and it has, also, various trade names such as "activator" and "thriftivator." When the clothes have been washed and rinsed, water is removed from them to a "damp dry" condition by the centrifugal force created by the relatively high-speed spinning of the entire tub or basket. The spinning is in a plane parallel to the floor.

The tumbler-type washer uses a revolving cylinder or drum for both washing and damp drying. The rotation of this cylinder is in a plane perpendicular to the floor. Most tumbler washers are loaded from the front but some can be loaded from the top. During the washing action, the cylinder revolves slowly, tumbling the clothes about in the soapy water. During the damp-dry cycle, the cylinder revolves rapidly and centrifugal action, again, helps to throw the water out of the clothes.

Regardless of the type of washer, successful washing action depends—naturally

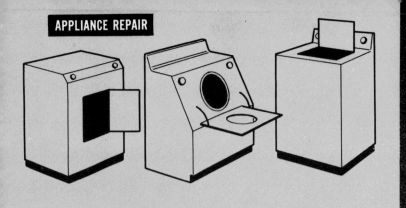

—on proper use of the machine. Of course, you (or whoever uses the machine) will follow the directions in the Owner's Manual. The clothes must be properly sorted as to type of fabric, colors, etc., and divided up into loads of eight to nine pounds (dry weight) for the average machine. Other requirements are: adequate supply of water at the right temperature; a good detergent, and soft water. As with any appliance, it goes without saying that the electrical wiring should be adequate to supply the required current at the rated voltage of the washer. Failure to provide the washer with proper working conditions and ingredients will, of course, result in improper washing results.

In this respect, a special consideration for agitator washers (most of them) is that the clothes should be more or less evenly distributed around the agitator. If there is an extreme unbalance of the load of wet clothes when the tub goes into the spin-dry action, it will vibrate unduly. Many machines have a safety switch which shuts the washer off if vibration due to unbalanced load gets too severe.

The heart of the washer is an electric motor, usually a split-phase induction motor of about 1/3 h.p. As a rule, the washer is belt-driven from the motor through pulleys. In the cylinder (tumbler) type of washer, the low speed for washing and the high speed for damp-drying are provided by the gears in a transmission, very similar to the function of the transmission in your car. In a similar manner, there is a gear-shifting arrangement and a clutch to engage the gears.

Most agitator washers have not only a high speed for spinning the tub in the damp-dry action, but also a slow-speed oscillating (back-and-forth) action for the agitator during the wash period. The Frigidaire washer, described in detail later in this chapter, imparts an up-and-down motion to the agitator. The ABC washers do not oscillate the agitator, but rather provide a slow-speed, off-center (eccentric) motion to it.

The two-speed transmission of a tumbler washer such as the Bendix described in this chapter is rather simple in principle: if the driven gear were the same size as the driving gear, it would run at the same speed; if it is larger than the driving gear, it will run at a slower speed, and if it is smaller than the driving gear, it will run at a higher speed.

To impart oscillating action, an arm (sometimes called a Pitman arm or Rack-bar) is connected off-center to a low-speed gear wheel. As the wheel turns, it imparts a back-and-forth motion to the arm. This motion is transmitted to a pinion gear (see illustration) which drives the agitator. A similar mechanism (rack and pinion) is often used to transmit the circular motion of an automobile's steering wheel to side-to-side motion of the front wheels.

On this type of (agitator) washer, a direct (steadily rotating) motion must also be provided to spin the tub or basket for damp-dry. Some sort of clutch action disengages one set of gears and engages the other. The clutch may be a friction (disc or plate) type, as is often found in cars, or it may consist of a pin dropping in place in a hole in the driven gear to engage it.

An important part of all washers is the pump, also deriving power from the motor, which pumps the water out of the tub. On the Bendix washer described in this chapter, the pump is on one end of the motor and the transmission is on the other end. The pump is always operating when the motor is running, but does not pump water out unless the drain valve is open. On other types, such as the ABC washer illustrated later, the pump is connected to the motor by a belt.

The pump is usually an "impeller" type,

which is simply a vane, like a small water wheel. If the pump becomes jammed by a foreign body such as a safety pin or a button, it can stop the whole washer in some cases.

Hot and cold water is fed into valves in the washer which turn them on and off and mix them at appropriate times. Although a few washers have thermostatic control over the water temperature, most work on a simple "on-off" principle. That is, when the hot water is on and cold is off, the water is hot—whatever temperature your tank provides (usually about 150° is recommended). When both hot and cold are on, they are evenly mixed to provide "warm" water. With average cold water temperatures out of the tap (about 50°), the mixture comes out at about 100°.

Clutches, gear-shifters and valves are usually operated by "solenoids." By definition, a solenoid is a cylindrical coil of wire which, when an electric current passes through it, acts as a magnet. In a typical application, a plunger would be drawn down into the solenoid when it is energized by a switch closing, which allows current to flow through the solenoid. The plunger might actuate a clutch, a valve, a brake, etc.

This is similar to the action of the starting relay which is described in the chapter on refrigerators and, in fact, the relay is a type of solenoid. The application is different, however. The relay is simply a magnetic switch, which opens and closes an electrical circuit, whereas the solenoids we are describing here do work—they impart motion to a mechanical part.

The final important element of the washer is the control. Part of the control is selected by the user—as for instance, washing time and water temperature—while the balance is automatic. Most of the automatic action is performed at certain pre-selected time intervals and the control is often called the timer.

The commonest timer is a set of cams operated by a smaller clock motor. Cams are irregularly shaped wheels. As they rotate, a bump or a depression on them will open or close a switch. Each cam is set to do its work at a different time, but they are all on the same shaft. The same thing happens in an auto engine, where a set of cams on the camshaft open and close the intake and exhaust valves of each cylinder at pre-determined intervals.

A different, but similar, type of timer is the "Time-line" control on the Norge washers. A clock motor rotates a long screw. As this screw rotates, the cycle control "carriage" progresses its length in a horizontal direction. Brass "fingers" on the carriage feel raised or depressed portions of the Bakelite terminal board behind it, and close or open electrical circuits as they do.

Here is a typical set of operations for a cam-operated tumbler washer. When turned on, a cam operates switches which start both the washer motor and timer motor. A second cam operates a switch which energizes a water-inlet valve. On the Bendix machine shown later in this chapter, a water float-switch cuts off the water when it reaches a certain height (just as the float in a toilet turns off the water when

(A) Revolving agitator, (B) Oscillating agitator, (C) Pulsating agitator, (D) Wobbling Basket type.

Top view of conventional agitator type (Whirlpool) shows water emerging from built-in lint collector.

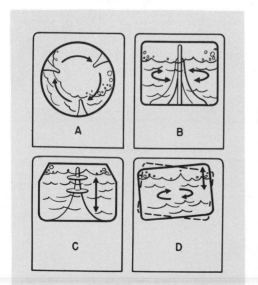

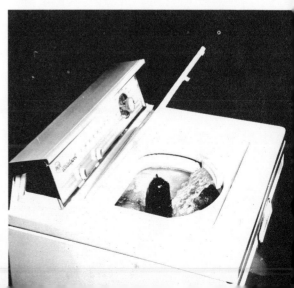

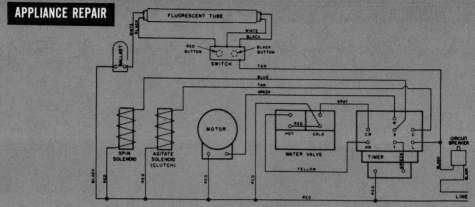

Wiring diagram for a Hotpoint agitator washer shows how timer controls all wash operations electrically.

it gets high enough in the tank), regardless of whether the inlet valve is open or not.

When the washer completes the wash cycle, another cam will then close a switch which energizes the drain valve solenoid, which in turn empties the sudsy water from the cylinder. A spray rinse may be provided to help clear the machine of suds, and a short extractor (spin dry) period is provided. Then the drain valve is closed and rinse water enters, after which the drain valve opens and the water is spun out. This operation may be repeated two or three times. Finally, the machine shuts off. On some—especially agitator types— a brake stops the tub from spinning after it is shut off.

Many variations of this pattern are offered in various washers, of course, but the general principle is always similar. At certain intervals a timer triggers off various switches which energize solenoids which in turn move valves, clutches, controls, etc. The user can vary these operations by setting the time for washing and selecting the water temperature desired. On many machines it is possible to stop the machine and repeat a cycle or skip one.

A variation in the speed-change opera-

tion is found on the ABC washers, among others—motor rotation is reversed.

One of the basic service tests which was discussed in an earlier chapter is continuity checking. On a machine with a number of automatic functions, the principle is the same, but the method has to take into consideration the number of circuits which exist and the timing which turns them on and off. An electrical diagram for one washer is shown here. If we wished to test—for instance—the agitate solenoid, we would have to check its electrical connections for the presence of voltage at a time in the cycle when it was supposed to be on. In an agitator washer, as a general rule, the agitator will never run unless there is water in the tub. This is to prevent tearing the clothes. Therefore, we would not expect the agitator solenoid to be energized until the water in the tub had risen to normal height.

A trouble-shooting table follows which outlines the test and service procedure for all common faults on a number of specific washers. As can be seen from the similarity in many of these procedures, they can equally apply to a different make of washer of the same type. •

Below, two types of agitator gearing to convert rotary motion of motor into oscillating motion.

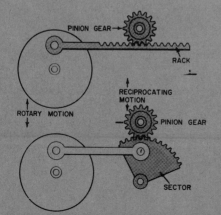

Most common type of timer has set of cams turned continuously by small motor. Each controls switch.

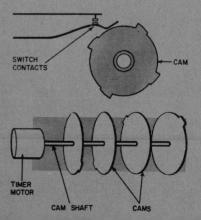

WASHER TROUBLE MASTER CHECK LIST

1. Motor does not run
A. No electric power to motor
1. Fuse blown.
2. Loose or broken wiring.
3. Vibration switch open (agitator washers).
4. Inoperative timer.
5. Defective motor.

B. Motor has power, will not turn
1. Pump jammed due to foreign object.
2. Transmission jammed.
3. Overloaded washer (usually happens in spin cycle).
4. Low voltage.

2. Motor runs but agitator doesn't
1. Belt off pulleys.
2. Faulty timer.
3. Loose connections (timer or clutch solenoid).
4. Clutch loose.
5. Broken gear in transmission.
6. Broken belt.
7. Loose pulleys.

3. Motor runs but cylinder doesn't (tumbler washers)
1. Belt off pulleys.
2. Belt broken.
3. Loose pulleys.
4. Clutch spring broken or clutch binding.

4. Washes, but does not spin
1. Off-balance load (agitator washers).
2. Water in tub due to plugged or inoperative pump.
3. Faulty timer.
4. Faulty clutch or transmission.
5. Brake faulty (stuck "on").
6. Basket loose.

5. No water enters tub (house water supply OK)
1. Clogged screen in water valve.
2. Loose connection to inlet valve solenoid.
3. Defective solenoid.
4. Float switch stuck open.
5. Valve stuck.
6. Defective timer.
7. Defective water temperature switch.

6. Water won't shut off
1. Inlet valve stuck open (look for sand, rust or dirt inside.
2. Float switch defective.

7. Water doesn't drain or drains slowly
1. Drain valve or screen clogged.
2. Water pump dirty or defective.
3. Drain hose plugged or kinked.
4. Defective drain solenoid.
5. Defective timer.
6. Pump belt broken, loose, or pulleys loose.
7. Defective agitator solenoid; pump will not run if agitator is operating.

8. Noisy operation
1. Loose brake hub, motor pulley, drive pulley or pump pulley.
2. Pump bushings worn or excessive vertical play in impeller shaft.
3. Basket drive tube loose (agitator washers).
4. Loose transmission gears or linkage.
5. Vertical motion in agitator shaft.
6. Dirt in motor pulley clutch (ABC).
7. Ticking noise—caused by unbalanced load (agitator washers).
8. Loose cabinet parts.
9. Cracked belt.

9. Leaks water
1. Door or lid gasket loose or dried out.
2. Cylinder back seal defective (tumbler washers).
3. Pump seal or cover gasket defective.
4. Hose connections loose.
5. Machine overloaded with detergent.
6. Door or lid out of alignment.

10. Leaks water through center of washer (agitator type) due to not draining
(see "water doesn't drain or drains slowly")

11. Water drains during washing (cylinder washer)
1. Drain valve stuck open.

12. Washer skips spray rinse (Bendix) due to not draining
(see "water does not drain or drains slowly")

13. Insufficient water extraction
1. Washer overloaded.
2. Tub or basket does not get up to speed.
3. Poor draining (see #7).

14. Excessive vibration
1. Worn belt.
2. Pulley out of round.
3. Motor shaft bent.
4. Floor weak.
5. Washer not setting squarely on all 4 legs.
6. Unbalanced load.
7. Cylinder shock absorbers loose or defective.

15. Washer creeps on floor
(see excessive vibration)

16. Incorrect water temperature
1. Hoses reversed.
2. Leads switched from water temperature selector to valve solenoids.
3. Valve or valve solenoid defective.
4. Supply of hot water is exhausted.
5. Water temperature selector switch inoperative.

17. Stalls while running
1. Off-balance load.
2. Improper adjustment of vibration switch; cuts out too soon.
3. Bearing dry or frozen.
4. Transmission or pump jammed.

18. Tears clothes
1. Use of liquid bleach in concentrated form.
2. Clothes catch under agitator which is loose or set too high.
3. Rough spot in cylinder.
4. Agitator oscillates without water in tub.

19. Agitator operates while basket spins
1. This is OK on ABC washer.
2. Broken or defective clutch.

This new model Bendix revolving cylinder automatic retains identifying round "window" shown.

Photos by Simon Nathan at Johnson Murphy Co.

Stuck float valve or water-level switch can be detected by moving up and down as shown above.

Below: removing solenoid assembly from water mixing valve. Note belt drive for wash cylinder.

Mixing valve plungers are seen as they enter solenoid. See page 66 for photo of solenoid removal.

BENDIX

Report by Ed Campbell

ONE of the earliest automatic washers was the Bendix. In fact, to many people, "the Bendix" is synonymous with "the washing machine." The classic Bendix is a rotating cylinder (tumbler) type washer with a round window in the front, and we have devoted considerable space in this section to that type of washer because there are so many of them in use. Today Bendix (now known as Philco-Bendix) makes several other types of washers as well.

As seen in the sketch on the right, the tumbler machine has a perforated washing cylinder inside of a stationary cylindrical tub. The washing cylinder is driven by a belt from the transmission which is permanently attached to the back end of the motor. This is a 2-speed transmission which is shifted by a solenoid attached to the outside of the transmission case. The low speed is for washing, the high speed for damp drying.

On the other end of the motor is the impeller-type water pump which helps evacuate the water which is spun out of the tub. Attached to the pump casing is the drain valve and the solenoid which opens and closes this valve. The pump runs whenever the motor runs, but the water is pumped out only when the drain valve is open.

On the back of the machine are the hot and cold water inlet hoses, which attach to the mixing valve. Solenoids operate the hot and cold valves to provide hot water or warm (mixed) water, as explained earlier in this section. The float switch,

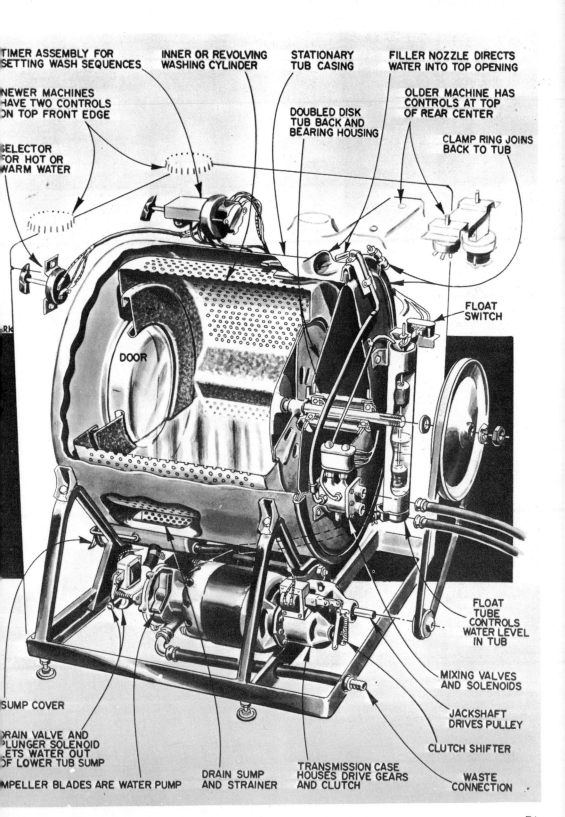

TIMER ASSEMBLY FOR
SETTING WASH SEQUENCES

INNER OR REVOLVING
WASHING CYLINDER

STATIONARY
TUB CASING

FILLER NOZZLE DIRECTS
WATER INTO TOP OPENING

NEWER MACHINES
HAVE TWO CONTROLS
ON TOP FRONT EDGE

OLDER MACHINE HAS
CONTROLS AT TOP
OF REAR CENTER

DOUBLED DISK
TUB BACK AND
BEARING HOUSING

SELECTOR
FOR HOT OR
WARM WATER

CLAMP RING JOINS
BACK TO TUB

FLOAT
SWITCH

DOOR

FLOAT
TUBE
CONTROLS
WATER LEVEL
IN TUB

MIXING VALVES
AND SOLENOIDS

JACKSHAFT
DRIVES PULLEY

SUMP COVER

CLUTCH SHIFTER

DRAIN VALVE AND
PLUNGER SOLENOID
LETS WATER OUT
OF LOWER TUB SUMP

IMPELLER BLADES ARE WATER PUMP

DRAIN SUMP
AND STRAINER

TRANSMISSION CASE
HOUSES DRIVE GEARS
AND CLUTCH

WASTE
CONNECTION

Above: solenoid would be removed if defective or if inlet valves need repair or replacement.

Replacing door gasket, necessary if leaks are not due to slow draining or high-sudsing detergents.

Head-on view of transmission, shows screwdriver on clutch adjustment screw. Pulley is at right.

seen to the right of the large pulley, cuts off the water flow into the tub when it reaches the right level, by opening the circuit to the inlet-valve solenoids.

The timer controls the sequence of events in the wash-rinse-dry cycles. The timer consists of a small motor which drives four cams, concentrically mounted on a single shaft. The cams are arranged to open and close various switches in a pre-arranged sequence. The first cam operates a switch which turns on the washer motor and the timer motor. The switches operated by the other three cams energize solenoids which (a) open or close the inlet valves, (b) open or close the drain valve, (c) by-pass the float switch during the spray-rinse and (d) shift the transmission to low or high. Functions "a" and "b" are controlled by the same cam and switch.

The water temperature selector switch provides either hot or mixed (warm) water. The timer switch can set the timer for various washing periods for different types of fabrics.

The "wash" cycle on this machine can be preceded by a "soak" cycle if the user wishes, and so sets the timer dial. This is more or less a repetition of the regular wash cycle except that warm (not hot) water is used.

A knowledge of a typical set of cycles will be useful in analyzing any trouble which might arise. Here is what happens: when the timer is set for "soak" or "wash," the first cam turns on the switch which

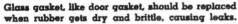

Glass gasket, like door gasket, should be replaced when rubber gets dry and brittle, causing leaks.

Inlet hose connections, as well as drain, can vibrate loose in time, can occasionally leak.

starts the timer motor and the main washer motor. At the same time, the water inlet valve opens and admits whatever temperature of water has been selected. When the water reaches the right level, the float switch de-energizes the inlet valve solenoid and the water stops coming in. At this point the user adds soap. At the end of the washing time which was selected by the user, the drain valve solenoid is energized and the water drains out. The next position of the cams causes the spray rinse to go to work (from the top) to wash the suds out of the cylinder. Then the shifter solenoid is energized to switch gears into high and water extraction occurs due to centrifugal force.

Then the motor is shifted back into low and the rinse water enters. The drain valve is, of course, closed. At the appropriate point, the float switch turns off the water, the drain valve opens and the motor shifts into high for a second spin-dry. This rinse-drain-extraction cycle is repeated once more and the washing is done; the washer turns off.

If the washer will not run at all and not a sound—no clicks or humming—comes from it, it is most likely not getting electric power. Check fuses first, and AC supply to the motors next. Remember that the washer motor and timer motor are both energized simultaneously when the timer is turned to "soak" or "wash." If, when the timer switch is rotated through its positions, clicking can be heard, you know that

juice is getting to the solenoids. So an open in the motor or to the motor is suspected.

If the motor hums but won't start, it might be due to the motor itself or the load connected to it. The first step is rotate the motor with your hand, with the switch off to see if it turns freely. If it does, check the motor for opens, shorts and grounds as described in the chapter on motors. If it does not, you must find out what it is that is holding it back.

Remember that something is connected to both ends of this motor. The transmission is on one end and the pump on the other. The pump is the most likely offender, so we'll start there. Why? Because it frequently gets jammed with something like a safety pin, buttons, marbles and the like. When it is jammed, it keeps the motor from turning because it is directly connected to it.

Since the drain valve and drain valve solenoid are connected to the pump, it is necessary to remove them to get at the pump, as is shown on pages 70 and 71. The obstruction will most likely be obvious when you open up the pump but, just to prove it to yourself, start the motor while the pump is disconnected.

If water does not enter the tub, the inlet valves or the mixing valve solenoids might be suspected and they can be removed .

But the float valve is more likely to be the trouble. It may be stuck open. When you actuate it with your finger as shown in the photo, it should move freely. Remember that this control consists of both a mechanical device and an electrical switch, either of which may be stuck open.

If water will not stop coming in even when the machine is turned off, the inlet valve is stuck open by some obstruction. If the water will not stop coming in *except* when the machine is shut off, the offender is the inlet valve solenoid, which is stuck closed—or the switch which controls it is stuck closed.

If the motor runs but the wash cylinder does not turn, the fault is in the linkage between the motor and the cylinder. Either the belt is broken or it is badly worn and is loose or one of the pulleys is loose on its shaft. A last possibility would be in the transmission itself, or the clutch.

If the water does not drain from the tub, it may be that the drain valve solenoid is not being energized by its switch or, if it is, it may be stuck open. If it moves freely with the current off and with its arm disconnected from the valve itself, we would suspect that the valve is stuck shut or that (a) the valve is clogged, (b) the valve screen is clogged, (c) the drain hose or the

Above: adding oil to transmission. Oil filler plug is in left hand, near shifter solenoid.

Left: large pulley which drives the washing cylinder, connected to transmission by rubber belt.

drain is plugged. Any can cause trouble.

If the washer leaks water or oil, it should be an easy matter to locate the exact place where it is leaking. And the solution is equally obvious. If the washer leaks from the door, it may be that the door or glass gaskets need replacing (see page 67), that the machine is flooding because the float valve or switch is stuck open, or that the machine is overloaded with suds due to the use of a high-sudsing detergent.

If the water temperature is correct at your water supply but not in the washer, you would want to make sure that the inlet

hoses are properly connected (hot to hot and cold to cold) and that the temperature control switch is OK.

If the water drains slowly, an obstruction in its path is likely. Slow draining could be due to clogged drain hose, strainer or pump. And if the water drains slowly, the machine may skip the spray rinse because it is still draining when the time comes for the rinse.

The hardest job the motor has to do is to spin the wet clothes at high speed for the extraction, or damp-dry period. If the machine is overloaded (more than nine pounds of wash) and/or if the drain isn't working or isn't working properly, the load may be too much for the washer motor. If so, it will labor at the instant that the clutch shifts it into high speed. The fuse may blow. Or the motor may fail to get up to speed sufficient to disengage the starting winding. In the latter instance, the motor would run hot and the thermal overload protective device would turn it off. Many tumbler-action (rotating cylinder) washers—although the one illustrated here is not one—will not go into high speed if the tub isn't drained.

If the shifter solenoid is stuck open, of course, it won't shift out of low gear. In other words, it won't enter the spin cycle. On the other hand, the washer might stay in high gear if the solenoid were continuously energized. A frequent cause of this trouble is an unintentional internal ground in the solenoid. This fault could occur with any of the solenoids.

Almost all complaints of failure of this washer to get the clothes clean are due to improper use of it. The user should follow the Owner's Manual to the letter, of course. The washer will fail to do a good job if it is overloaded, if the water is not hot enough or if there is not enough hot water (from your hot water tank); if the water is not soft enough (water softener required); or if the right quantity of the right type of detergent is not supplied. This type of washer (tumbler) does not want a high-sudsing detergent.

Troubles in the machine which would cause poor washing would be mostly confined to drain troubles. As explained above, slow draining might cause the washer to skip the spray-rinse cycle, which might mean that all the soap or detergent is not washed out of the clothes.

Although many other particular makes of washers are described in this chapter, this section may be considered typical of the rotating cylinder type. Bendix does make an agitator washer, which will be

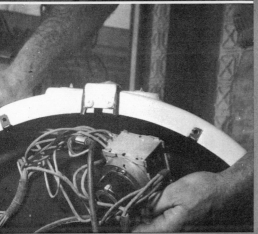

Top: tightening or removing drive pulley requires an Allen wrench. Pliers here is for added leverage.

Bottom: removing the timer assembly. Small end is the motor, square part holds gear and 4 cams.

Pictures on these two pages show steps in removal of the pump. Since drain valve and its solenoid are in the way, they must come off first. Above, wires are removed. Below, end view of solenoid and valve.

described in a moment, but it is not as typical of agitator washers as some of the other brands which will be described, because of its use of the collapsible tub for water-extraction.

If any parts need to be replaced on your washer, you should try to get exact factory replacements. Look up "Bendix" (if that is your brand) in the classified phone book and find the factory branch or authorized parts distributor. Be prepared with the exact model number and/or any other descriptive information you can find on the machine, if you have to buy belts, gaskets, valves, gears, etc.

If any parts are disassembled that contain gaskets (such as the transmission), it is always a good practice to put in new ones. Gaskets make a good seal because they have a certain amount of resilience which is squeezed when the bolts are tightened up. They seldom can be re-used, as this resilience doesn't last forever.

When gears are replaced because of worn or broken teeth or other troubles, all gears which operate together should be replaced at the same time—especially if the washer is two or three years old. A new gear in which a set of old ones is apt to be noisy and/or make a poor fit.

New door gaskets usually come rolled inside out, and they are "rolled on" to the door. Belts are removed or replaced on this washer by turning the large pulley counterclockwise while removing. Tension should be adjusted for perfection.

Above, left and right: removing drain valve solenoid after valve rocker arm has been disconnected.

Below: water pump disassembled for cleaning. Impeller is in foreground, beside drain solenoid.

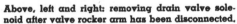

The Bendix top-loading agitator type washer is one of two brands (ABC being the other) which reverses the direction of the motor to shift from high to low. It is the only machine which squeezes the water out of clothes instead of spinning them dry. A collapsible tub inside the main tub is pumped down to a partial vacuum after the water has been drained off. The wash is therefore squeezed dry against the agitator. If this bag (tub) were to develop a leak, it would, of course, tend to oppose the attempt of the pump to get the air out of it.

As in the tumbler washer, both the pump and the transmission are connected to the motor, but in this case via belts instead of directly. The drive pulleys for these two devices contain clutches which operate centrifugally in one direction only. One works clockwise, one counterclockwise.

The agitator in this (Bendix) washer can be removed (and should be cleaned off from time to time) by removing a cap on the top. If the cap is not tightly in place, the agitator can bounce, resulting in noisy operation of the washer. •

refrigerators
FREEZERS AND AIR CONDITIONERS

REFRIGERATORS, freezers and air conditioners all operate according to the same principles, and an understanding of refrigeration principles and their application to these devices can be interesting as well as useful. They all operate to remove heat and, to a certain extent, moisture from the atmosphere. Some of the basic axioms of physics are involved in the process.

The first of these is that heat tends to flow from the warmer to the colder body. In doing so, the warmer body gives up some of its heat and the temperature of the colder body is raised. In other words, heat is removed from the warmer body. In a refrigeration system, the heat comes from the food, from the water in the ice trays, from the air when the refrigerator or freezer door is open, and from the air to the air conditioner.

The cold body in the refrigerating system is a chemical refrigerant, flowing through pipes in the system. In all modern refrigerators, this refrigerant is one known as Freon-12 or F-12. This is a colorless, odorless liquid which boils at 22° below zero under normal atmospheric pressure. In other words, above that temperature it is converted into a gaseous or a vapor state.

The air or atmosphere exerts a pressure on everyone and everything, which at sea-level is 14.7 pounds per square inch. As we go up in altitude, the pressure gets lower.

We can increase pressure above atmospheric only in a confined space, such as a tank, and we do this by means of a pump called a "compressor." We can also remove the pressure from a confined space by exhausting the air from it, and we do this by means of an "exhaust pump." Absence of normal pressure is called a vacuum, or partial vacuum. Light bulbs and radio tubes enclose a vacuum.

Some interesting things happen when we start fooling around with pressure. For instance, in a given space (or volume), such as a rigid tank, if we increase the pressure, the temperature increases also, and in direct proportion. On the other hand, if we have a certain volume of gas enclosed in a tank at a certain temperature and pressure and we release it into a larger space, the temperature and the pressure go down.

As we shall see, this is roughly what happens in a refrigerating system: the refrig-

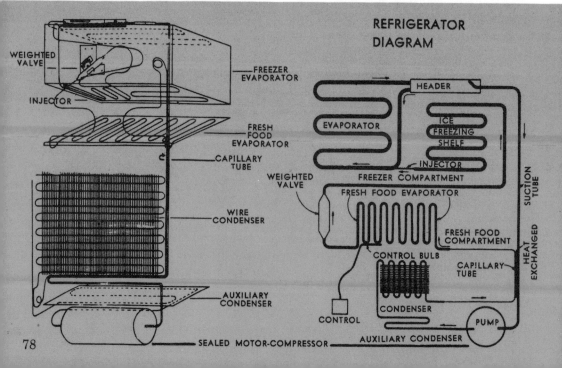

REFRIGERATOR DIAGRAM

WEIGHTED VALVE

INJECTOR

FREEZER EVAPORATOR

FRESH FOOD EVAPORATOR

CAPILLARY TUBE

WEIGHTED VALVE

WIRE CONDENSER

AUXILIARY CONDENSER

SEALED MOTOR-COMPRESSOR

HEADER

EVAPORATOR

ICE FREEZING SHELF

INJECTOR

FREEZER COMPARTMENT

FRESH FOOD EVAPORATOR

FRESH FOOD COMPARTMENT

CONTROL BULB

CAPILLARY TUBE

CONDENSER

CONTROL

AUXILIARY CONDENSER

PUMP

SUCTION TUBE

HEAT EXCHANGED

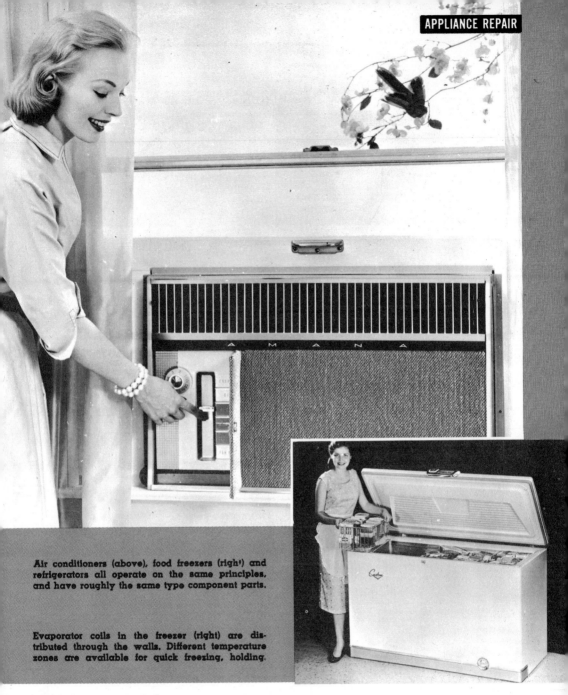

Air conditioners (above), food freezers (right) and refrigerators all operate on the same principles, and have roughly the same type component parts.

Evaporator coils in the freezer (right) are distributed through the walls. Different temperature zones are available for quick freezing, holding.

erant is pumped or compressed to a high pressure and temperature and then released so that its pressure and temperature drop. The cold refrigerant passes through the freezing coils and removes heat from the food, water and air in the compartments of the refrigerator. In doing so, it warms up. It is then recompressed and the process starts over again.

Here are a couple of more common principles used in refrigeration: when a liquid evaporates—that is, changes from a liquid to a vapor—it has a cooling effect. You can see this if you wet your hand in a breeze. As the water evaporates from your hand, it cools it. The faster a liquid evaporates, the more cooling it effects. Thus, ether evaporates very fast and will almost freeze your hand if you put some on it.

The air (atmosphere) will only hold a certain amount of water vapor at any particular temperature. The higher the temperature, the more water vapor the atmosphere will take. But at any tempera-

Hermetically-sealed motor-compressor (above) cannot be serviced, but is relatively trouble-free.

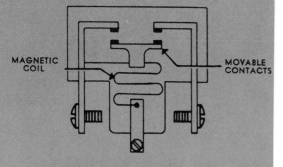

MAGNETIC COIL

MOVABLE CONTACTS

Starting relay is shown in open, or running position. When closed, it connects motor start-winding.

ture, there is still a limit. That is why, on hot, humid days, water doesn't evaporate easily—there's no place for it to go. Ordinarily, our perspiration evaporates and cools us. But on humid days, it can't evaporate, and consequently we feel uncomfortable.

It follows that if the temperature of air were reduced, it couldn't hold as much water vapor, and consequently some of this vapor would have to return to the liquid state—or in other words, condense. When warm, moist air hits a cold glass in the summer, the temperature of the air right at the glass is suddenly reduced and moisture condenses on the glass. This principle has two consequences in refrigeration and air conditioning. First, let's take refrigerators.

The food we put in the refrigerator contains moisture and the air which enters when the door is open contains moisture. Remember that heat goes from a warm body to a colder one. So when the moisture-laden heat goes to the cold coils or plates of the refrigerator, water condenses on them. The water freezes, causing "frost" in the refrigerator. Various devices and systems have been contrived to melt this frost and get rid of the water but some

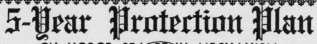

5-Year Protection Plan
ON NORGE SEALED-IN MECHANISM

FIVE-YEAR PROTECTION PLAN—WE WARRANT to the original purchaser the Sealed-In mechanism of this Norge Household Rollator Refrigerator to be free from defects in material and workmanship under normal use and service, and we will, within five years from date of delivery to the original purchaser, replace without any cost to the customer, any Sealed-In mechanism which our examination shall disclose to our satisfaction to be thus defective. The foregoing applies only to the Sealed-In mechanism under conditions specified herein, and does not apply to any other parts of the Norge equipment mentioned hereinafter.

ONE-YEAR WARRANTY—WE WARRANT to the original purchaser this Norge Household Cabinet, Norge motor controls and starting equipment, to be free from defects in material and workmanship under normal use and service, and we will replace without any cost to the customer, within one year from date of delivery to the original purchaser, any Norge part or parts thereof, which our examination shall disclose to be defective. After one year from date of delivery to the original purchaser, a charge may be made for service calls and adjustments (other than the replacement of the SEALED-IN MECHANISM as stated in the Five-Year Protection Plan above), whereby the Norge is made to operate satisfactorily, and for any repairs to the cabinet, its finish, the Norge motor controls and starting equipment.

This warranty is in lieu of all other warranties express or implied and of all other obligations or liabilities on our part, and we neither assume nor authorize any other person to assume for us, any liability in connection with the sale of this NORGE Household Rollator Refrigerator. This warranty shall not apply to said refrigerating equipment or any part thereof which has been subject to accident, alteration, abuse or misuse.

The term "original purchaser" as used in this warranty, shall be deemed to mean that person, firm, association or corporation for whom the refrigerating equipment referred to herein is originally installed.

This one-year warranty and five-year protection plan shall apply only within the boundaries of the continental United States. This warranty shall be void if any alteration is made on the warranty certificate.

MODEL NO.................... CABINET NO....................

Name of Original Purchaser

Street   City   State

Installation Date

Signature of Norge Dealer

NOTE:—This warranty shall not be in full force and effect until completely filled out and signed by Norge Dealer at time of sale and delivery to original purchaser.

NORGE DIVISION Borg-Warner Corporation
DETROIT, MICHIGAN

Howard E Blood
President

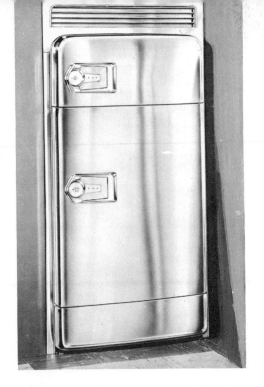

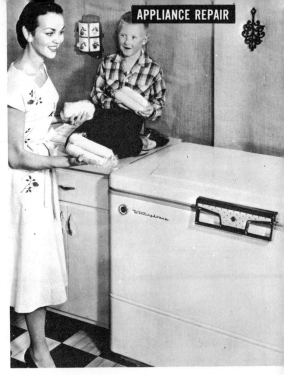

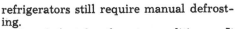

Condenser needs good ventilation. This "built-in" refrigerator-freezer has ventilating louvers above.

The proper preparation and placement of fresh foods is necessary for satisfactory quick freezing.

refrigerators still require manual defrosting.

Now let's take the air conditioner. It exposes its cold coils to the air and the air gives up heat and is cooled. The heat removed is blown outdoors or is transferred to water and carried away. It follows that when the air is cooled, its capacity to hold water vapor—or in other words, to be "humid"—is reduced, and water vapor condenses to a liquid.

So you might say that it is an accidental benefit of air conditioners that they also reduce the humidity. Actually, in very humid locations, this virtue is as important as removing heat, as far as physical comfort is concerned.

The ability of either the refrigerator, freezer or air conditioner to remove heat is limited to the physical capacity of the compressor and the motor which drives it, and is carefully and precisely figured out. The amount of heat which can be removed in a given length of time is called the "heat load." You can overload a refrigeration system with heat just as you can overload an elevator with weight, so that it can't get off the ground floor.

Overloading is uncommon with refrigerators, except when ventilation is so restricted that they can't get rid of the heat

Below: electric wiring diagram for a Norge refrigerator. Heaters are for defrosting, butter keeper.

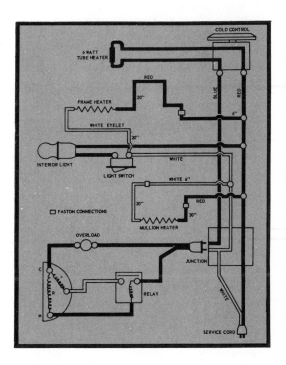

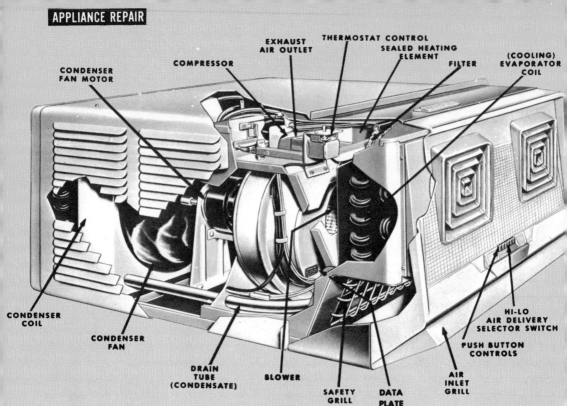

they remove. Overloading air conditioners is more common, however, as mother nature is somewhat unpredictable. The required capacity of an air conditioner can be precisely figured out and provided for—and usually is with a central unit. But with window air conditioners, people usually buy what they feel they can afford, and often the capacity for cooling isn't sufficient for the job.

The essential components of any refrigerating system are (1) the compressor and the motor which drives it; (2) the "liquid line," which carries the high pressure, high temperature refrigerant away from the compressor; (3) the condenser—a system of coils exposed to the air, and from which heat is given off; (4) the evaporator, or cooling unit, where the now-cold refrigerant takes heat away from the food or water to be cooled and is itself warmed up in the process; (5) the "suction line," which returns the refrigerant to the compressor. The liquid line is on the "high side" (high pressure side) of the compressor, while the suction line is on the low side.

Earlier refrigerators had an "open unit." That is, the compressor and motor were separate and accessible underneath the refrigerator, and the motor was connected

to the compressor or by a simple belt drive.

Modern refrigerators have a hermetically-sealed unit, in which the motor and compressor are—as far as the owner is concerned—permanently enclosed and sealed up.

External to this unit are the various components described above, with variations from brand to brand and model to model. In addition, there is a cold control (or controls), a light bulb, and sometimes heating units for defrosting and for maintaining a slightly higher temperature in a "butter keeper."

It is customary for the warranty on a refrigerator to distinguish between these components. A typical warranty, illustrated, provides a 5-year warranty on the sealed unit and a 1-year warranty on the cabinet, motor controls and starting equipment. Read the words in your own warranty; they may also say, "This warranty shall not apply to said refrigerating equipment or any part thereof which has been subject to accident, alteration, abuse or misuse."

The control unit is a thermostatic device, of course. The temperature of the evaporator is "sensed" by a small metal bulb attached to the freezing shelf or compart-

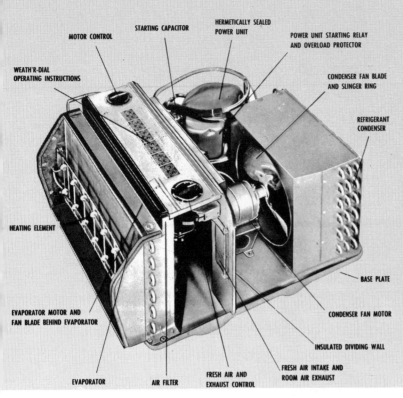

WEATH'R-DIAL
OPERATING INSTRUCTIONS

MOTOR CONTROL

STARTING CAPACITOR

HERMETICALLY SEALED
POWER UNIT

POWER UNIT STARTING RELAY
AND OVERLOAD PROTECTOR

CONDENSER FAN BLADE
AND SLINGER RING

REFRIGERANT
CONDENSER

Mitchell Mfg. Co.

HEATING ELEMENT

BASE PLATE

EVAPORATOR MOTOR AND
FAN BLADE BEHIND EVAPORATOR

CONDENSER FAN MOTOR

INSULATED DIVIDING WALL

EVAPORATOR

AIR FILTER

FRESH AIR AND
EXHAUST CONTROL

FRESH AIR INTAKE AND
ROOM AIR EXHAUST

Window air conditioner, like refrigerator shown on page 122, has sealed unit, evaporator, condenser. Some have heating element for winter use.

ment. This bulb is connected by a tube to the thermostat and the whole assembly contains a small amount of refrigerant. As the refrigerant expands or contracts due to varying degrees of cold, the thermostat opens or closes a switch to turn on the motor-compressor. The setting of the cold control determines the temperature at which the thermostat will try to hold the evaporator, by cycling the compressor on and off.

While most open-unit refrigerators use capacitor-start motors, the sealed-unit boxes usually use a "starting relay" for the motor. A relay works on an electro-magnetic principle.

When a motor is turned on, it draws a high current in an attempt to start. This current passes through the coil of the relay, exerting magnetic force which draws the "points" together. This closes a circuit which puts the starting winding of the motor in business, and the motor starts. As the motor picks up speed, the current drops, the magnet lets go and the starting winding is cut out. The motor keeps running on its main winding until the thermostatic switch turns it off.

Food freezers operate in the same manner as refrigerators except that the tem-

peratures are lower and the layout of parts may be different. Air conditioners also operate in the same manner, but have no "freezing compartment." A typical window unit would have the evaporator inside the room, with a fan to blow cold air in; the condenser would be outside the window, with a fan to help remove heat from it. Usually the sealed unit is also located outside.

There are two things which can cause trouble in any of these units: one is low line voltage due to inadequate wiring, the other is improper ventilation which prevents proper heat removal. In the first instance, the motor will draw too much current and will stop due to the thermal overload protector. In the second instance, the compressor will run excessively without adequate cooling and may eventually kick out due to thermal overload.

Warm air leaking in through the door can cause excessive running and inadequate cooling. This is due to a poor seal around the door. As the cabinet ages, the gasket (usually rubber) dries out and loses its resilience. An exact replacement can be obtained from the distributor of your brand. If the refrigerator is not level, the door hinges will gradually be warped,

SCHEMATIC DIAGRAM OF BASIC FREON CIRCULATION CYCLE

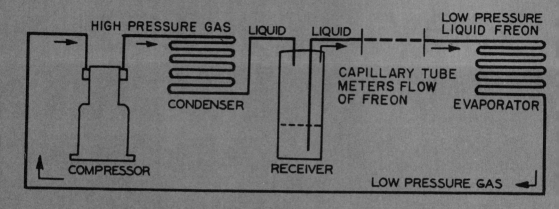

and the door will not make a good seal. Being out of level can also cause improper drainage of defrost water on some models, and improper evaporation of defrost water.

If the refrigerator does not run, we must consider that there are two switches controlling the unit, either one of which may be defective. One is the thermostat and the other the starting relay. If the box were warm and definitely should start, these switches can be quickly checked by shorting them out (one at a time) with a "jumper" wire.

If the thermostat is faulty, and the trouble is not due to the control bulb having become separated from the evaporator, and is not due to faulty electrical connections, then it would have to be replaced. The same philosophy applies to the relay.

If it can be determined that current is reaching the motor and it will still not start, the trouble is inside the sealed unit, and factory service would be indicated. Of course, a complete continuity check would have to be run on the wiring to determine this.

If the relay is stuck closed, the starting winding would never kick out, the motor would run hot, and would stop due to the thermal overload protector. If the relay sticks open, the motor would not start.

If the condenser coils become clogged up with dirt and dust, air circulation will be inhibited and therefore heat loss reduced. The unit will run more often and may cool inadequately. If the evaporator is thickly covered with frost, heat removal from the box will be inhibited because the frost acts as an insulator.

Since it is not possible for the home handy man to service the compressor nor

any of the refrigerant lines, he must try to determine by a process of elimination whether these are at fault. We will sum up most of the points which he can check:

1. Line voltage is normal (110-120 volts).
2. Cabinet is level.
3. Adequate ventilation for condenser.
4. Condenser coils are not obstructed by dust and dirt.
5. Door seal tight.
6. Freezer compartment door seal tight, if there is one.
7. Starting relay OK, nut stuck open or shut.
8. Thermal overload protector not stuck open.
9. Door not being left open too long and too often.
10. (Thermostat) control bulb not detached from evaporator.
11. Thermostat cuts in and out OK.
12. Electrical continuity throughout the system.
13. Cold control properly set.

We have explained how these faults, if they exist, would affect operation of the refrigerator or freezer.

An air conditioner does not have doors, of course, but it does have a starting relay and sometimes also a thermostat. The heat load on an air conditioner may be more than it was made to carry, which could cause improper cooling. Heat losses can be cut down by insulation; by sealing up windows; by shielding windows from direct rays of the sun by awnings (and especially, shield the evaporator of the unit itself); and by cutting down the introduction of heat and humidity when the outside heat is at its height. This means from cooking (especially boiling water), taking

84

showers, doing laundry, etc. Exhaust fans to carry heat directly outdoors can help prevent heat build-up on the inside.

The fans on an air conditioner require periodic oiling and of course, the filter requires periodic replacement or cleaning.

Considerable trouble from all three refrigeration-type appliances can be eliminated by a careful reading of the instruction book and careful adherence to the operating instructions therein. This suggestion is particularly pertinent in connection with air conditioners and their capacity to cool.

The capacity of a cooling system is usually stated in "B.T.U. per hour." B.T.U. means British Thermal Unit, and it is a measure of heat—the amount of heat required to raise 1 pound of water 1 degree Fahrenheit. B.T.U.'s can be removed, as in a refrigerator, or added, as by a heater.

The computation of B.T.U.'s is complicated and is done according to standards agreed upon by an industry. Most of us never know about or care about these things. We buy a refrigerator or freezer for its cubic feet of storage capacity with the assurance that under correct and normal operating conditions, it has sufficient capacity to handle what goes into it.

But on air conditioners, its a different story. Air conditioners were formerly rated in horsepower or in tons and there was a rough correlation between the two and between the actual capability of the machine. As new techniques and developments came into use, these terms were found inadequate. Now many units will be found rated in B.T.U. Here are some examples of current products:

Vacuum cleaner is ideal for removing dust and dirt which collects on condenser, hindering air motion.

Louvers or holes in the cover should also be perfectly cleared to insure good air circulation.

Brand "A" model 1—¾ H.P.—6,500 B.T.U. per hour
Brand "A" model 2—¾ H.P.—8,200 B.T.U. per hour
Brand "B" model 1—¾ H.P.—6,600 B.T.U. per hour
Brand "B" model 2—¾ H.P.—7,500 B.T.U. per hour
Brand "C" model 1—¾ H.P.—5,650 B.T.U. per hour
Brand "D" model 1—¾ H.P.—9,150 B.T.U. per hour
Brand "B" model 3— 1 H.P.—9,000 B.T.U. per hour
Brand "C" model 2— 1 H.P.—7,900 B.T.U. per hour

This very short list will show that it is no longer possible to buy air conditioners according to horsepower ratings. A "bargain price" air conditioner is very likely to be one of the lower-rated models.

Certain generalities can be stated concerning the capacity in B.T.U. required for a certain size room but such generalities are affected by outside temperature, height of ceiling, type of insulation, number of windows, exposure, etc. If you are in doubt, your dealer can show you how to estimate your heat load. •

toasters
WAFFLE IRONS AND GRILLS

These are resistance-heating appliances, which convert electric energy into heat. Each has a "heating element," utilizing wire of relatively high and very accurately measurable resistance.

RESISTANCE-HEATING appliances convert electrical energy into heat, which may be used to toast bread, grill hamburgers, press clothes, warm a room, etc. Heat is developed by passing current through a special type of wire which has a higher resistance to the passage of electricity than the ordinary wire used in attachment cords. Overcoming this resistance causes heat. You might imagine it to be the result of electrons of current forcing their way through densely crowded molecules in the wire, resulting in friction, although this is not an accurate technical description of what happens.

Typical attachment cords on portable appliances have a resistance of about 4 ohms per 1,000 feet. In a 6-foot cord, therefore, there would be about 24/1000 (.024) ohms resistance, which is so small as to be unmeasurable by ordinary means. For all practical purposes, this is a short circuit.

The resistance of any wire depends on its length, cross-section (diameter), material used (copper, aluminum, etc.) and temperature. A typical heating coil wire similar in size to the attachment cord just described, but different in material, has a resistance of .398 ohms per inch of coil. This is 4,776 ohms per 1,000 feet, or approximately *1200 times as great* as the resistance of the attachment cord.

A 33-inch length of such wire, having a resistance of 13.2 ohms, would develop 1,000 watts of heat on 115-volt current. The current drawn would be 8.7 amperes. This is typical of the element in a grill or waffle iron.

For any given size of such heating wire, the watts consumed and the current drawn can be accurately determined from the length of the wire. Here are some ex-

Old-fashioned non-automatic toaster has no means of controlling either time or amount of heat.

Typical automatic "pop-up" toaster uses thermostat to control color of toast, turn off heat.

Most toaster elements consist of ribbon-type nichrome wire, wound around sheets of mica.

Waffle makers and grills usually have elements of coiled nichrome wire, rather than ribbon-type. The coiled wire concentrates a greater amount of heat because it contains more wire to the inch.

A third type of heating element is the "Calrod" unit, such as is used in electric ranges (above). This type of unit consists of a coiled nichrome wire inside a metal sheath, and well insulated.

amples, based on the same wire just described, which has a resistance of .398 ohms per inch of ¼-inch coils:

Length in inches	Total ohms	Watts (at 115 volts)	Amperes
66.8	26.4	500	4.3
33.4	13.2	1,000	8.7
22.1	8.8	1,500	13.0

Thus you see that there is an inverse relationship between resistance and current: the lower the resistance, the greater is the current drawn and, of course, the wattage consumed. The advantage of the resistance wire used in this example is that the heat is confined to a relatively small area.

The wire is an alloy of nickel and chromium, as a rule, with trade names of Nichrome and Tophet. This wire is used both coiled and flat (ribbon). The figures given above were for inches of close-wound coils with a coil diameter of ¼ inch. The resistance of the flat or ribbon type is a good deal lower. Typical ribbon found in toasters has a resistance of about .05 ohms per inch. Thus it would take 264 inches of such ribbon for a 1000-watt element. This is not difficult to attain in a 2-slice toaster, which has four element assemblies, each of which can accommodate about 12 rows of ribbon.

The ribbon isn't actually lower in resistance than the coiled wire—it just seems that way because there is more wire in an inch of coil than in an inch of ribbon. Toasters usually employ ribbon-type heating wire, while waffle irons and grills use coiled wire. Coiled wire is also used in many rotisseries, heater-fans and hot plates. Some electric flatirons use ribbon elements, while some use coiled wire specially wrapped in an insulating sheath.

"Calrod" heating elements are used in electric ranges, some rotisseries and some flatirons. Calrod is a trade name for a heating element consisting of coiled nichrome wire inside of a metal sheath (usually copper). The element is packed inside with a material which not only holds it in place but electrically insulates it from the sheath. These units are sometimes round and sometimes flat. They have the advantage of being rugged physically, easy to keep clean, and shock-free to the touch.

From the table above, it can be seen that the resistance of an electrical circuit limits the amount of current drawn, and therefore the watts consumed. It follows that a short circuit or partial short, since it would lower the resistance, would greatly increase the current. A blown fuse would probably result. It is also apparent that if we could, by means of a switch, select different quantities of heating wire, we could vary the heat developed. This is often done in waffle irons, which have two sections of heating wire, separately controlled.

Another pertinent fact is that the watts of heat developed depends on the voltage. Here are some typical examples:

Resistance of Element	Line Voltage	Watts	Amperes
13.2 ohms	100	757	7.57
13.2 ohms	110	916	8.32
13.2 ohms	115	1,000	8.69
13.2 ohms	120	1,090	9.08

This table demonstrates why low line voltage, due to inadequate or overloaded house wiring, can cause a slowdown in the operation of resistance-heating appliances. It would take 25% more time to make a piece of toast on 100 volts than it would on 115! However, since your electric meter is operated by current flow (amperes), the difference in cost between the 100-volt and 115-volt operation would be only 12.8%.

The simplest toaster—the old manual type—had a single heating element in the middle. This consists of a piece of mica (a good insulator) around which the ribbon-type heating element was wound. Most 2-slice automatics have four such slabs, one on each side of each piece of toast. In addition, they have a timing device which turns them off when the toast is done.

The toaster is normally in an "off" condition. The switch is closed when the toast

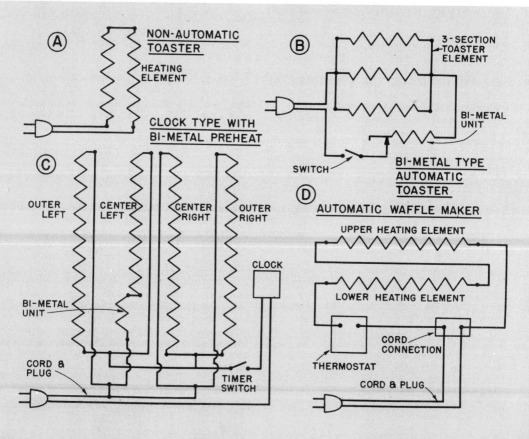

A — NON-AUTOMATIC TOASTER
HEATING ELEMENT

B — 3-SECTION TOASTER ELEMENT
BI-METAL UNIT
SWITCH
BI-METAL TYPE AUTOMATIC TOASTER

C — CLOCK TYPE WITH BI-METAL PREHEAT
OUTER LEFT / CENTER LEFT / CENTER RIGHT / OUTER RIGHT
BI-METAL UNIT
CLOCK
CORD & PLUG
TIMER SWITCH

D — AUTOMATIC WAFFLE MAKER
UPPER HEATING ELEMENT
LOWER HEATING ELEMENT
THERMOSTAT
CORD CONNECTION
CORD & PLUG

is depressed into the toaster. The timer is a small alarm clock which, instead of ringing a bell, releases a spring which causes the toast to pop up. When the toast is up, the switch is again in the "off" position.

Because not everyone likes toast the same way, and because some types of bread toast faster than others, a color control for the toast is provided. This adjusts the time which will elapse before the clock kicks off.

When the toaster is cold, it takes longer to heat than when it is hot, so the third piece of toast is apt to be darker than the first. This is sometimes overcome by a bi-metal delay device. Here's what happens:

The clock is pre-set for operation when the toaster is hot. The delay device prevents the clock from starting its cycle until the toaster gets hot. But when the toaster is hot, the time delay no longer operates. Therefore, toasting time is automatically adjusted to the heat of the toaster.

The bi-metallic element—which is used in many types of appliances and also in the thermostat for a furnace—consists of two strips of metal fastened together. Two different metals are used hence "bi-metal," or "two metals." Every metal expands at a different rate when exposed to heat and so one of these two wants to expand a lot more than the other. Since they are tied together, they fight each other and the result is a sharp bending under heat. This bending action can be very accurately determined.

Using the bi-metal as a switch, we can consider it normally open. When it bends to a certain degree, it makes contact with the other side of the switch, and the switch is closed, or "on." If it cools a little bit, it begins to go back in place again, and the switch is opened. This switch, however, does not turn the current on and off, but merely actuates the timer.

Not all automatic toasters use a clock timer. Some operate purely on the thermostatic principle of the bi-metal, which in this case *does* act as a switch to open and close the circuit.

Manual toasters can only have trouble due to an open circuit in either the cord or the heating element. A simple continuity check can determine this, and the offending part is replaced. Don't try to repair a heating element.

Automatic toasters are more prone to mechanical troubles than electrical ones but there are a few facts you should know about the electrical circuit in case you should experience trouble in that quarter. Two-slice automatics have either 3 or 4 heating elements: one on the outside of

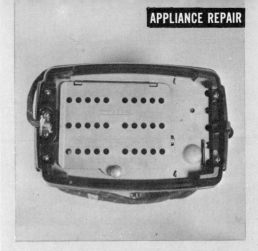

First step in toaster disassembly is to remove the case, usually by removing screws on bottom.

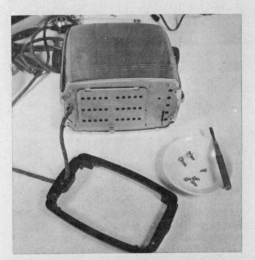

It's a good idea to put all screws and parts in a dish or cup as removed. Above, toaster base off.

Chromium sections of the case usually slip apart after the base is removed, exposing the elements.

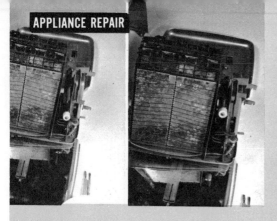

Left: bread carrier depressed, contact "points" are closed. Right, carrier up, points are open.

This Universal toaster, shown here with its cover removed, uses a clock mechanism to time the toast.

each slice and one double-faced element in the middle, or two single-faced ones. These elements are wired in parallel.

Consequently an open in a heating element would not render the toaster inoperative, as would be the case in a series-wired device. If one element opened up, the others would still work, and you would be able to see which one was at fault.

If the toaster won't work at all, therefore, the trouble is ahead of the heating elements: either in the plug, cord, connections within the toaster, the switch, or the breaker points which are opened and closed by the switch.

The breaker points may become dirty or pitted and require cleaning. Dirt —and especially crumbs—can cause many troubles in the toaster mechanism, and one of your first acts should be to get it good and clean.

If you should have to replace an element in an automatic, it is important to get an exact replacement. The center element or elements do not have the same wattage as the outer ones (they can get away with less heat because heat is not conducted away from them so quickly) and the whole assembly of 3 or 4 elements is carefully coordinated to produce the name plate wattage and current consumption when the voltage is within prescribed limits (110-120).

Most automatic toasters fall into one of the categories we have described, with some added refinements. That is, there is the simple clock-timer type, which should be pre-heated before any toast is put in. The addition of the bi-metallic delay element to this type eliminates the necessity for pre-heating. The straight bi-metal type of toaster has no clock and depends for its "timing" on the heating and cooling of a bi-metal strip. There is another type of toaster which is actually sensitive to the color of the toast. The heat from the element is reflected to a bi-metal from the toast itself. The darker the toast, the less heat it will reflect.

A good deal of the repair of mechanical troubles in these toasters is "cut and try." First, the mechanism must be exposed. The toaster case consists of three sections which are tightly fitted together and held in place by the base, which is screwed on. The knobs must first be removed, then the bottom screws, then the base and finally, the case will come apart. Connections should be inspected as well as breaker points and, as stated earlier, everything should be cleaned and free of crumbs.

It can happen that when you take the toaster apart, a small spring falls out. The question is, "Where did it come from?" Only a very careful inspection can tell you, and a manipulation of all moving parts for freedom of action and apparent "normality."

While all makes and models of toasters differ from each other to a certain extent, the Universal toaster shown is typical of a large percentage of those in use. The bi-metallic element of this toaster is—or should be—adjusted so that the clock will go into operation in from 30 to 50 seconds at normal room temperatures. If the toaster is adjusted for "light" toast the clock will run for from 10 to 50 seconds; if set for "dark," it will run between 1' 45" and 2' 30 seconds. If there is anything wrong with the clock, it should be replaced. Efforts to fix it will consume a lot of time and are not likely to be successful.

Two screws on the bottom of this Universal toaster hold the bi-metal securely in place. If the preheat time is over 50 seconds, one loosens these screws and positions the bi-metal strip so that it won't have to travel so far before it releases the brake on the clock.

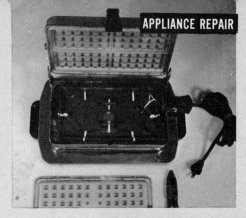

Terminals for connection of line cord to heating element are also exposed when case is removed.

Lower element of a combination waffle-maker and sandwich grill is typically of coiled nichrome.

A typical waffle iron is pictured here with one section of heating element exposed. A similar arrangement is found in the top half of this appliance. Whereas the toaster used nichrome ribbon as a heating element, the waffle iron utilizes coiled wire. The heating wire is kept in place by ceramic spacers. There are both non-automatic and automatic waffle irons. On either type, there is usually an indicator of some kind to tell the user when the iron is hot enough to put the batter in. This indicator is, of course, basically a bi-metal type. On the automatics, a thermostat controls the baking time selected by the user and an indicator light shows when the waffle is done.

In general the operation of waffle irons is very simple and little trouble is ever experienced. Usually the upper and lower units are in series and, of course, an open anywhere would make the appliance inoperative. The most common source of such trouble, outside of the line cord, is the section of wire running from the bottom section to the top. This wire is subject to considerable flexing and bending, and is likely to eventually develop an open. A point-by-point continuity check will reveal if this is the location of the trouble.

The thermostat keeps the waffle maker at a pre-determined temperature during the cooking cyle. The thermostat might be stuck open, which could cause the unit to be inoperative. Loose connections and/or shorts at the thermostat terminals are frequent sources of trouble. If the thermostat is defective, it should be replaced rather than repaired.

Probably the most universal complaint with waffle irons is not that they won't work, but simply that the waffles stick to the grids. This is probably because people don't read the instruction book, or else because this booklet has long since been lost

Before the waffle maker is used, it should

Below, top: timer mechanism from a Camfield toaster; bottom, a replacement coiled-wire element.

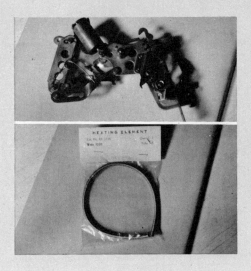

be pre-heated and then coated with a thin film of lard (not butter). Then one waffle should be cooked and discarded, as it has absorbed the excess oil. The grids are now conditioned and no further application of oil should be used. After using, the grids should be wiped clean with a damp cloth but should not be washed in soapy water, as this will remove the oil film. If for any reason the grids must be washed, they must be reconditioned as before.

Sandwich grills are exactly the same as waffle irons in operation and, as a matter of fact, many have flat grids which are interchangeable with waffle grids. Electrically and mechanically, testing and repair is the same. But the flat grids do not require the conditioning or care of the waffle grids and may be washed like any other cooking utensils. •

91

electric irons

AND OTHER HEATING UNITS

THE TWO MAIN TYPES of electric flatirons are non-automatic and automatic irons. The former has no control over the heat developed, other than shutting it off, while the latter utilizes a thermostatic control to maintain the heat selected. Steam irons and combination steam-and-dry irons follow the same general principles of ordinary irons. Travel irons are merely more compact in size and are usually non-automatic. Non-automatic irons usually run 500 to 600 watts, whereas automatic irons run to 1,000 watts and over.

The heating element in an iron is usually one of three types: nichrome ribbon wound over a mica sheet, nichrome coils permanently built into the sole plate, and Calrod units cast into the sole plate. Usually only the first-named type is replaceable and most of the newer irons have non-replaceable units.

The heating element is, of course, insulated from the sole plate and all other non-current-carrying metal parts of the iron. On a non-automatic iron, the leads from these elements are brought right out to the connection studs where the line cord is attached. On an automatic iron, the thermostat is in series with the element and the cord.

The familiar "iron plug" is fast disappearing, the cord instead being permanently attached to the iron. With an automatic iron—the most popular type—it is hardly necessary to disconnect the iron.

The principal seats of trouble in an iron are (1) in the cord and its plug or plugs; (2) in the connections to the element and thermostat; (3) in the thermostat and (4) in the heating element. The first two are guilty about three-quarters of the time.

The usual continuity or test-meter checks will unearth many of the more common troubles. As shown here, a test lamp may be used to check the cord when the latter is plugged into the wall. This method cannot be used, of course, if the plug is permanently built into the iron. In this case, you would have to go directly to the inside of the iron.

If the cord is OK and if the iron is not automatic, the trouble must be either in the connections to the element or in the element itself. The connections should be visually inspected for intermittents, opens, and corrosion, as well as obvious breaks. If the element is open or is partially shorted and cannot be replaced, a new sole plate is indicated.

If the element is of the replaceable type, care should be taken to make clean, strong connections, avoiding accidental shorts and grounds. The iron should be tested for shorts and grounds after the replacement is made. A new element is apt to smoke a bit when first turned on because of the cement used in it, but this will go away.

There are many types of thermostats used on irons but the general principle of operation is this: a switch—usually consisting of breaker points—is made of a stationary metal strip and a movable strip. The latter is a bi-metal strip. The switch is normally closed when the iron is cold, unless the control knob has an "off" position. When the bi-metal reaches the operating temperature selected by the user, the bi-metal strip warps, opening the contacts. As it cools, it again closes. When it reaches temperature again, it opens. This continuous cycling tends to maintain the temperature of the sole plate within relatively narrow limits—or in other words, virtually constant.

The temperature at which the iron will hold can be adjusted by pre-setting the thermostat by means of a temperature-selector knob. This moves the fixed side of the switch in such a way as to narrow down or increase the area in which the bi-metal element is free to move. The shorter this distance, the more often the iron will be "on," and therefore the hotter the temperature it will maintain.

The chief troubles with thermostats are mechanical. They may get bent or they may just get old and lose their resilience. They may be stuck open or stuck shut. Sometimes cleaning the breaker points will help them. But generally, the thermostat should be replaced if there is anything seriously wrong with it.

An internal short or ground may cause

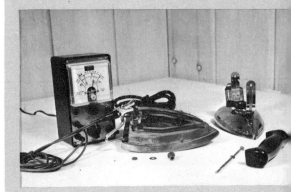

Checking the element connections of the iron bellow, here with cover removed, using meter-tester.

Above, conventional automatic dry iron with thermostatic control and cord that plugs onto iron.

Casco automatic combination steam-and-dry iron has cord permanently attached to body of iron.

With iron cord plugged into outlet, test lamp can be used to check the cord for electrical continuity.

With meter test prods on one end of iron cord, a low resistance reading would show short circuit.

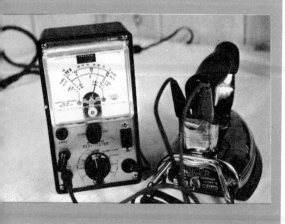

Meter reads 17 ohms on this 800-watt iron when test prods are connected to element via terminals.

the fuse to blow, may create shock hazard, or may cause the iron to get too hot and/or draw too much current.

In the tests illustrated, in which an iron is tested with a meter, the resistance is seen to be about 17 ohms when tested across the terminal posts. This is an 800-watt iron and by using the formula $R = E^2/W$ (where R = resistance in ohms, E = line voltage and W = watts), we find that the resistance should be:

$$R = \frac{(115) \times (115)}{800} = \frac{13225}{800} = 16.5 \text{ ohms}$$

Our reading of 17 ohms was well within the 10% accuracy we can expect of the tester, so we'll assume it to be OK.

In the next test, we took a reading between one post of the iron and the frame of the iron. There should be no connection between these two—in other words, we should get a reading of "infinity" or "open." However, we see that we got a reading of 20 ohms. This indicates that the element was grounded. Checking inside the iron, it was found that the ground existed at the terminal connections, and was easily removed.

In the next test, the current drawn by the iron (after the ground was cleared) was checked by taking the current for the iron right through the tester. The reading is 6 amperes. Using the formula $I = E/R$ (where I is the current in amperes, E = the line voltage and R = the resistance in ohms) we find that:

$$I = \frac{115}{17} = 6.7$$

This, again, is within the 10% accuracy of the instrument, so we find it satisfactory. And besides, since our resistance read a little high (17 instead of 16½) we would expect the current to read a little low.

In the tests on a disassembled iron shown here, the iron is of the type which has a coiled-wire heating element built into the sole plate.

Some irons have a fusible element which melts and opens the circuit if the iron gets dangerously hot. The iron should be inspected for such a fuse if the complaint is that it doesn't heat up at all.

When the cycling of an iron's thermostat causes the lights to dim and brighten up noticeably and annoyingly, it's probably an indication of inadequate wiring. A tiny bit of fluctuation is normal, but a great deal indicates overloading. Of course, before jumping to conclusions, it might be well to check the current drain of the iron. It might well be that a partial short inside is causing it to draw too much current.

A steam iron's problems are similar to a regular iron except that a few special troubles may be due to the water, the water reservoir and the water seals. Distilled water is recommended because it has no impurities which can cause deposits and corrosion in the iron. When ordinary water is used—and especially if it is hard water —the inside of the reservoir will develop scale and deposits, the valve may become clogged and the escape holes may become clogged. An overnight soak with vinegar inside may help to loosen up some of the deposit so it can be drained out. Visual inspection of the holes may indicate the need for cleaning. If the iron leaks, take it apart and inspect the gaskets and seals. It may be necessary to replace them.

On the Casco steam-and-dry iron illustrated—which is typical of currently popular irons—it is necessary to remove the control knob before you can get inside the iron. This is done by loosening a set-screw, which in this case calls for a small Allen wrench. It is then possible to get at the screw which secures the cover. The line cord must be released at the hole where it enters the cover, so that enough slack can be introduced for free inspection of the inside. The terminals and the thermostat are then revealed. This thermostat will turn the iron off, and you can demonstrate this fact by testing for continuity through the line cord while revolving the shaft of the thermostat from off to on. It would not be necessary to remove the water tank unless the iron were leaking, and it would not help any to do so in electrical servicing since this iron has Calrod units cast into the sole.

In this and the preceding chapter we have described several resistance-heating appliances: toasters, waffle irons, grills and flatirons. There are, of course, many others and they generally follow the same principles and have the same parts.

Other resistance-heating devices, such as hair dryers, tea kettles and fry pans will also follow the same patterns as the previously mentioned appliances. Heating pads and electric blankets do also, but we do not recommend that the reader service these two items. The danger of shock or fire due to a poorly repaired heating element in one of these is not worth risking. Electric water heaters and ranges are high-wattage units usually operated on 220-240 volt circuits. This is big-league stuff which should be handled by a qualified technician. It is the policy of this book not to recommend servicing of any of the "3-wire" appliances. •

The 800-watt iron draws 6 amperes when connected through tester, a normal value (see text).

Heater-fan utilizes heavy-gauge nichrome wire in large-diameter coils in sturdy heating element.

Another heating appliance, the bottle warmer, has coiled-wire heating element in base to heat water.

ALL ABOUT
clothes dryers

A GREAT LABOR-SAVER among the newer appliances is the clothes dryer, which removes moisture by tumbling the wash in a draft of hot air. A revolving drum powered by an electric motor provides the tumbling action, while the heat is provided either by gas or electricity.

Moisture- and lint-laden hot air is exhausted from the dryer (this is most comfortably and efficiently vented to outdoors) on all except one type of dryer, which washes the lint away with water. A lint-trap or lint-screen is provided and needs frequent cleaning. Obstruction in the screen or the vent will slow down the heat-and-moisture removal, could make the dryer inoperative.

The motor drives the drum by means of a belt. A broken belt, or one which has improper tension due to misadjusted pulleys, is a frequent cause of trouble. Like most other appliances, the dryer can experience trouble due to low line voltage. This is most likely on 120-volt dryers, and trouble would be most likely to manifest itself in the motor—which would run too slow and too hot and might stop due to throw-out of the thermal overload protector.

A worn or frayed belt could cause excessive noise as well as slippage, in which case the basket or drum would fail to come up to speed. If the belt were broken, the motor would run but the basket would not.

Most dryers have a high-limit safety control switch which turns the dryer off if the temperature goes too high. On Norge dryers, for instance, where the normal temperature is 110-150° Fahrenheit, this switch kicks out at 200°. It automatically kicks in again when the temperature goes down to 150°. Excessively high temperature, causing this switch to kick out, might be due to a plugged lint screen (preventing air exhaust), high line voltage or a broken belt.

If the motor does not run and the fuses are all OK, remove the line fuse (an important must before working on any appliance which is wired in rather than plugged in), disconnect the belt and the motor leads (connecting wires). Check the motor for continuity as explained in the chapter on motors. Even on 240-volt dryers, the motor is usua ly a 120-volt motor, AC, and usually the split-phase type. This means it has no brushes, and has a built-in centrifugal switch which cuts out the starting winding when the motor gets up to speed. On some dryers, the heating elements (almost always Calrod units) will not go into operation until the motor has gotten up to speed and the starting windings have kicked out.

If the motor runs but the cylinder does not, the belt is broken or there is trouble in the linkage: loose pulleys or broken motor-tension spring.

If the dryer runs noisy, the trouble can be a worn belt or loose pulleys; lack of tension on motor spring; loose (vibrating) parts anywhere in the dryer; or the dryer

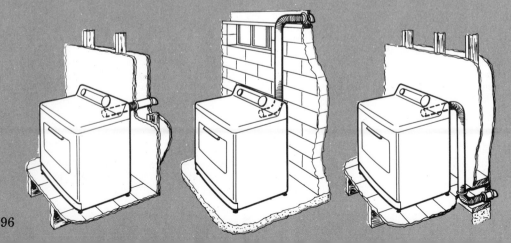

On most dryers except Hotpoint and Maytag, which flush lint away, a vent to the outdoors is recommended to carry off moisture- and lint-laden hot air. Shown are 3 alternative methods for venting.

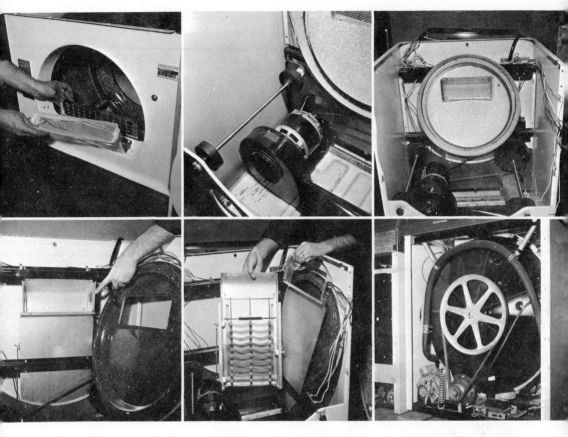

Top left: removing lint trap on a GE dryer for cleaning. Center: drum removed to show placement of motor. Right: rectangular screen is entry for hot air in this dryer. Bottom left and center show stages in removal of heating elements. At right, belt drive for drum of combination washer-dryer.

may not be resting securely on all four legs.

If the dryer is electric and it dries too slowly—and if the trouble is not a plugged lint screen—the fault may be in low voltage, a defective segment of a two-element heating unit or a faulty thermostat. With the fuse removed, the heating elements can be checked for continuity.

Checking the action of the thermostat is not within the means of the average home handy man, and a serviceman should be consulted if the trouble is isolated to this location.

Any type of dryer can be adversely affected in its operation by too heavy a load of clothes. Most dryers are designed to accommodate the load of an average

washer, which is 8-9 pounds of dry clothes. When the clothes come out of the washer, of course, they weigh more than that (about 14 pounds). If the washer fails to remove the normal quantity of water, the dryer will be overloaded and will be slow to dry.

Any type of vented dryer—gas or electric—will be adversely affected in its operation if the lint screen or trap is plugged. The type which does not vent away the moist, lint-laden air is known as the "condenser type," such as Hotpoint and Maytag. The moisture and lint-laden air is condensed to a liquid in a "condenser chamber" and washed down the drain by cold water, which provides the cooler temperature required for condensation. •

Getting Started

Here are important facts, typical setups to consider if you're just starting out in the aquarium hobby.

H. Degenhardt obligingly explains the qualities of various types of tanks at NYC's Midtown Aquarium. Note broad selection of foods and remedies.

Hal Kelly photos

UNLESS you're in the upper income brackets, the equipment and plants you "choose" to buy are pretty much decided for you by the amount of money you have to spend. When you start selecting fish, though, the situation is a little different. Many of the most attractive, interesting species are also the least expensive —and many of them, incidentally, are livebearers that reproduce cheerfully and prolifically. What this means is that you have tremendous room for choice, even on a limited budget.

Let's consider some of the factors, apart from cost and personal preference, that you ought to keep in mind when you begin to stock your aquarium. First of all, there's size. Fish are generally fond of eating fish, and you're asking for trouble if you put fish of widely-varying size in the same tank. Right off the bat you have to decide whether you'll keep small fishes, medium-sized ones or big ones. Another point in the same category is compatibility. Some breeds are far more belligerent than others and will attack fishes the same size or even larger than themselves. In the catalog sections of this book, we've put the finger on many of these scrappy species. If you're in doubt about the disposition of any fish, though, ask your dealer about it before you buy.

Another important consideration is temperature tolerance. If you want to avoid the expense of a heater and thermostat, you can still enjoy a successful home aquarium by limiting your selection to fishes that can stand a broad temperature range. You'll probably be surprised by the "tropicals" that can survive low temperatures.

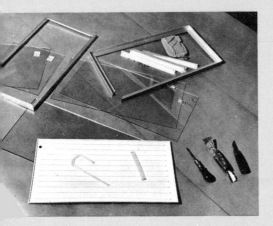

You can save money by building your aquarium from a kit like this manufactured by the Aljo Co.

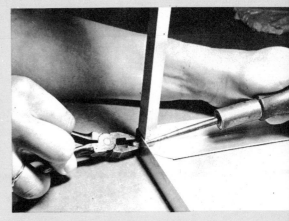

The first step in assembling the kit is to bolt the aluminum framework using a screwdriver, pliers.

After completing the framework, attach the bottom glass with aquarium cement. Press down as shown.

Cement front, back and side glasses to framework. Scrape off excess cement with your putty knife.

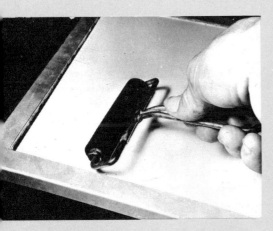

When you have finished the tank, you may wish to apply a decal. Roll wet decal on the back glass.

Note how decal of underwater scene gives tank an illusion of depth. Now aquarium can be filled.

Line bottom of tank with gravel. However, before pouring gravel in, wash it until water is clear.
Hal Kelly photos

Rocks and other objects used as aquarium decorations must be rinsed well to remove impurities.

Consider size of aquarium when choosing ornaments and, before placing in tank, wash carefully.

Unless you're a pretty exceptional hobbyist you won't want all your fishes to be bottom-feeding scavengers, or, for that matter, to be all surface-breathers either. You'll probably want some fishes that live on the bottom, some that inhabit the middle and upper portions of the tank, some bold types that prefer to swim in the open areas, and others that live among the plants. And no beginner's aquarium should be without at least one pair of live-breeding fishes. The pleasure of finding babies in your aquarium some morning just can't be equalled by any other aquarium event.

Before you buy every fish in sight though, consider carefully how dense a population your aquarium will stand. Aeration, of course, makes a world of difference in the number and/or size of the fishes that can be kept successfully in a given volume of water. Without it you must be especially careful of overpopulation; one fish too many in the tank and they'll all suffer from too much carbon dioxide, too little oxygen. It's wise to begin with a light population. You can always add, and an over-ambitious start can be hard on you, your budget, and the fishes.

To help the newcomer to the hobby plan his own aquarium, we have worked out a series of typical setups based on different cash outlays. The prices are those prevailing in California at the time of writing, and are subject to some variation due to season, freight costs, availability, and so on. But wherever you are in the U. S. these prices are going to be pretty representative.

$7.50 Set-up

The beautiful little one-gallon aquarium shown above contains eight active, colorful fishes. The tank itself is of good quality with a stainless steel frame, like the rest in these set-ups, and it costs $4.95 with full cover and light. Three Medaka fishes cost $1.00, three Guppys about 60 cents, two Zebrafish 80 cents. These fishes are all very temperature-hardy, and don't require a heater. Sand and plants account for the remaining 15 cents. Accessories that would be nice are a scraper for cleaning the glass and a dip tube for removing foreign matter from the water.

$15.00 Set-up

The set-up above uses a three-gallon tank with full cover and light, which sells for about $7.50. It allows 75 cents for plants and 15 cents for sand, leaving $6.55 to spend on fishes. To the $7.50 community above we could add, for example, two pair of Platys for color and a pair of Black Mollies, each fish costing around 70 cents. You still have fish that can tolerate a lot of temperature change and you can regulate the tank's temperature to some extent by switching the light off and on. In this selection you could leave out one pair of Platys, for example, and get instead a good scavenger like the Japanese Weatherfish.

$25.00 Set-up

The fishes in the set-up shown below would be approximately the same, but the tank size would be five gallons. This would cost about $9.25 with a full cover and light. For $25 you could also include a $6.95 pump and a $1.75 outside filter. The gain is in more room, plus an aeration and filter system. The fish will have more room in which to display themselves, the water will stay cleaner, and you'll have room and air for many more fishes when you're ready to add them. But you'll still have to stick to temperature-tolerant fishes. The background of the tank shown is a reproduction of a color photograph.

$50.00 Set-up

Now we're getting into the big time (see photo above). We have a ten-gallon tank, which, with its cover, costs $16.25. It's equipped with the same pump as the one above, and we've added a $3.75 sub-sand filter and a $6.70 heater and thermostat. About $4 is allowed for really beautiful plants, the effect of which is added to in the photo above by a silk-screened background of Vallisneria. Blowing $1.50 on good-looking gravel and rocks, we still have $11 to spend on fishes. You need not worry about temperature sensitivity, and the combinations you can work out for populating this aquarium are literally unlimited. Just as an example, you could have this good community: three Pristellas, three Pearl Danios, and a pair each of Black Banded Barbs, Skunk Catfish, Platy Variatus, Brass Tetras, and Australian Rainbows.

$100 Set-up

The magnificent aquarium below looks like a lot more than its actual cost and from the point of view of long-term family pleasure it's worth a lot more. You have a 25-gallon tank with cover, a big sub-sand filter, heater and thermostat, and the same pump as above. You can spend $10 or $12 on splendid, exotic plants and still have between $25 and $30 to spend on fishes. This is a fairly huge amount of money for the purpose, and just how to spend it is a problem. Here's one possible selection of 23 beautiful, interesting fishes for such an aquarium, based on spending as much as $3.50 a pair for some of them: one Whiptail Catfish and a pair each of Black Swordtails, Black Mollies, Gold Wag Platys, Kissing Gouramis, Elongatus Hatchetfish, Thick-lipped Gouramis, Hemiodus, Bloodfins, Rummy-nose Tetras, Rosaceous Tetras and Spotted Catfish. •

Marine Aquariums

Fans like the challenge of keeping a salt water
aquarium—and are paid off in spectacularly beautiful results.

MARINES ARE HARD TO HANDLE—
they make tough demands—they're
expensive to maintain. If you've been
around the aquarium hobby for any length
of time you've heard these objections—and
more—to keeping salt-water fishes. And
they're largely true. But the number of
marine aquarists multiplies every year.
What was once the exclusive territory of a
few specialists has become the hobby of
many "average" home-aquarium keepers.
Perhaps one reason is that these fans enjoy
solving the tricky problems they're bound
to run into—they like the challenge. But
probably a more important reason is that
the most spectacularly beautiful species of
tropical fishes are found in ocean water,
and a successful marine aquarium is a
dazzling sight to see.

In their home environment marine fishes
have no problems of overcrowding, plenty
of available live food, and water that contains just the right amount of salt. Dupli-
cating these conditions in your home re-

quires painstaking care and skill, but if you look at the pictures of the weird, wonderful, often bizarre varieties pictured here, and try to imagine how they look in brilliant natural color, you may well decide they're worth some extra effort.

A salt-water tank should be as big as you can afford to get, but not too big to move around and handle. It's best to have several tanks and keep one of them empty for emergencies. The material used in the tank is important. All metals in general use for aquariums—including stainless steel—can be corroded by sea water. If you use a tank with a metal frame its internal joints must be covered with a special cement. Some aquarists have used cement tanks for salt-water fishes with good success; others prefer all-glass containers.

Even more important than the tank is the water you put in it. The ideal answer is clean sea-water. If you have access to

the real thing, use it by all means, and store extra emergency supplies in glass acid carboys. To keep the percentage of salt in the water from changing, both in storage jars and in your tanks, you must mark off the exact level of the water when you first fill them, and from time to time, as the level drops through evaporation, bring it up again with fresh—preferably distilled —water.

If you can't get fresh sea water, there are a couple of alternatives you can try. You can buy a dry salt preparation and add it to fresh water and wind up with a fair imitation of sea water. Or you can buy concentrated ocean water, to which you also add fresh water. In either case you maintain the salt percentage at the proper point by adding more fresh water as evaporation takes place. A hydrometer, a device to measure water's specific gravity— which depends largely on the salt content

A salt water tank should be as big as you can afford to get, but not too big to move around or handle. The beautiful but over-sized tank shown here was photographed by Eccles in a Los Angeles Airport.

—is inexpensive to buy and helps you keep a scientific eye on the salt-percentage.

Except in very special cases, marine tanks must be aerated. Without plenty of oxygen sea water tends to acidify and if it does you're likely to lose the tank's population en masse.

Another source of acidity is the decomposition of droppings and uneaten food. This means you need either a filtering system or a great deal of enthusiasm for hand-siphoning. Even with a filter (glass wool, activated carbon and marble chips make the best ones) you have to siphon by hand every day in order to remove debris that's bigger than the filter can handle.

Just as fresh-water fishes feel more at home in a planted tank that gives them cover from real or imagined enemies, marine fishes need a place to hide, too.

Plants are seldom successful in salt-water tanks; rocks that you find on land often contain minerals that the fishes can't tolerate. Real ocean coral seems to work best. It must be completely clean and sterile—and should be used sparingly. Complicated coral mazes hide uneaten food and dead fishes and can become a source of pollution. The same is true of sand, which looks pretty but is practically impossible to keep clean.

Salt-water species prefer eating the kind of live food they find in the sea, but most of them will eat and thrive on brine shrimp and good dry food. Feed them sparingly at first to see how much they'll take. Then increase the diet, but *never* overfeed. This is an important rule for any aquarium, but it's crucial in the easily-fouled marine tank. •

Never keep live plants in a marine aquarium. Coral, as shown above, is best and should be thoroughly clean.

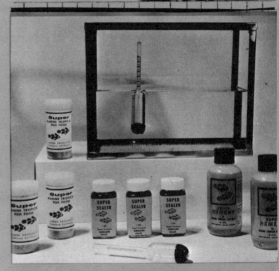

Marine fishes may be captured or purchased. Tank, left, contains clownfish, dascyllus, and coral cats.

Among equipment "musts": insulating Super Sealer, Super Remedy, hydrometer, and special Marine food.

Concentrated sea water and salts from which it can be "reconstructed" are available, but natural is best.

Making a Flight Bow

Few flight bows are commercially produced, and the construction of his own record-making bow is the dream of many an ambitious archer

The Yeoman flight bow at full draw. Angle shown is approximately correct one for maximum flight

THE flight bow is the ultimate in the bowyer's field. Many flight bows are made, shot once and then abandoned. Or, they may shatter during that single use and go into discard that way. Just the same, flight bows serve a valid purpose in the archers' world, for they are somewhat like the Formula cars in international racing—paving the way for future developments based on their performance.

To make a record-setting flight bow is the aim and dream of many a bowyer—a goal all too seldom realized. Because flight bows are the final word in bowyery they are seldom, if ever, commercially produced. You just cannot go into your nearest tackle shop and buy a flight bow. You may be able to have one made for you, if you're lucky, but essentially the flight bow is a personal thing. It conforms to you and to your ideas. It may be the result of months of planning and days of work and when once it's finished, you will be faced with the decision as to whether or not you'll overdraw just once, in the big gamble which may—or may not—pay off.

For these reasons, any plans for a flight bow must be offered somewhat diffidently. They are the end product of someone else's thinking—not yours—and they may not embody the ideas and principles which you, as a bowyer, feel are necessary for success. However, the bow which resulted from these particular plans is a lovely thing, light in the hand, sweet in performance with no harshness on the hand. Surprisingly enough, there seems to be no drastic stacking up at the end of the draw and there is comparatively little pinch. However, since all good flight shooting today is done by means of the hook, the matter of finger-pinch is relatively unimportant.

The plans have been designed by Frank Bilson, one of England's foremost archers, and in his capacity as head of the Yeoman Bow Company, a liveryman of the Worshipful Company of Bowyers. These then are the plans and specifications of the Yeoman Flight Bow (Copyright 1960)

Many flight bows, following the precedent established by the Turkish and Persian bowyers, carry the big *siyahs,* or ears, which impart additional impetus and cast. Now siyahs were developed long before our new synthetics and it is our contention that using modern fiberglass, it is no longer necessary to incorporate them in flight bow design. Since the siyah is not an integral part of the limb-arcs, it is slow moving in relationship to the bow itself. Thus, with the materials available today, i.e. those

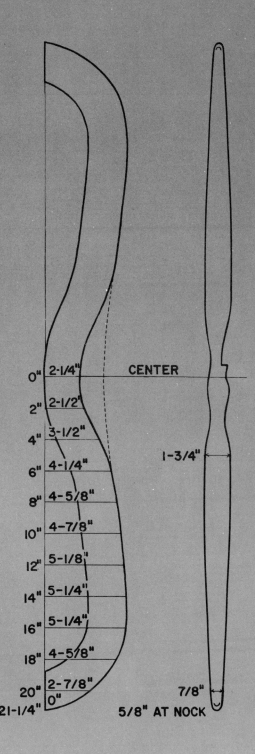

YEOMAN FLIGHT BOW. © 1960

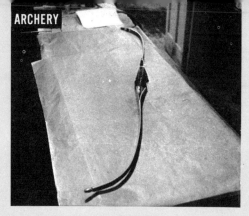

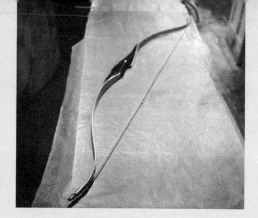

Elongated view of the bow shows powerful curves which impart cast; retain smoothness in shooting.

Here the bow is braced. Comparison shows way in which power is converted within bow when braced.

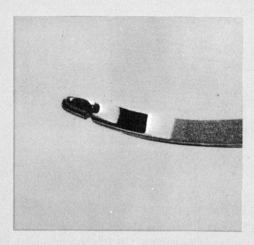

Ornamental nock beautifies bow. Thin strips of plastic strengthen any inherent weakness in bow.

View of the braced bow, showing a part of upper limb cut away to form "semi-center shot" section.

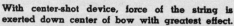

With center-shot device, force of the string is exerted down center of bow with greatest effect.

This is a view of the finished handle of a good target bow. Also shown is laminated handle riser.

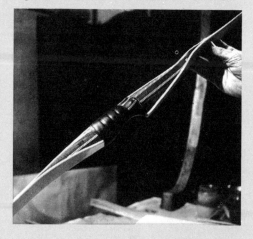

The "feather" arrow rest is seen above. This is great aid to efficient use of plastic fletchings.

After taking laminated bow from clamps, excess glue must then be removed from handle and limbs.

which inherently do the work formerly given to the siyah, the addition of the ears results in a lowered performance.

Dr. Paul Klopsteg has advanced the theory that the ideal bow for cast would be based on the principle of the uncoiling arc. These plans are adaptations of his theory using fiberglass both for the backing and the facing in the two limbs.

MATERIALS

For a 48" bow you will need the following materials:

Four (4) Maple Laminations 24½"x1⅞". The taper on these should run from .68 thousandths of an inch down to .45. An additional .15 thousandths will give you, in your finished bow, an increased draw weight of approximately 20 pounds. Thereafter the draw weight increase is partially nullified by the mass increase.

One (1) Handle Riser. This should be of any good hardwood, with walnut being a good choice. 8½" in length, the riser tapers at both ends.

Four (4) Fiberglass Strips 24¼"x1⅞". Personally I prefer Bo-tuff, but any similar material can be used. Get strips which measure .40 thousandths in thickness.

Twelve (12) C-clamps. Glue. Urac-185 by preference. One (1) Former. See instructions which follow. Rubber wrapping. Thin plywood battens. Grease-proof paper.

INSTRUCTIONS

The former is cut according to the scale shown. Your material is any block of sufficient length and thickness, free from knots and twists. The basing line, along which the inch-stations are located, should be perfectly flat. If a block of sufficient thickness is not available, you can make one by gluing sheets of plywood together in order to get the right dimension. The width must be a minimum 1¾" and it may be advisable to have it an inch wider. Since this is a one-step glue-up, you can use the spare width to place brads, in order to hold the materials in position.

When the former is cut, you can rout out the excess material along the base line so that the jig follows the working area. This is not essential, but unless you are using extra large C-clamps, it will facilitate the clamping. Be sure that the working surface is absolutely flat and free from splintering.

Cover the former with two layers of your grease-proof paper, holding it in position with Scotch tape or thumb tacks. This will keep the bow from sticking to the jig with any expressed glue.

Prepare the fiberglass and the laminations carefully. The pair of lams which will be on the back of the bow will have a ½" overlap at the center and accordingly must be feathered or chamfered to form a smooth overlay. Set up your series in a dry run, clamping as you go so that when you are ready to glue you will know what you are doing.

With the backing down and the first pair of lams, you are ready to set the handle riser. Since this block will come above the line of the bow belly the lams and glass will not meet over it and they must be feathered down to lie as smoothly as possible.

Having finished your dry run, you will now do your actual gluing up. There are six surfaces to be covered—the insides of the glass and both sides of the laminations. Make sure that with the latter the taper runs along the outside of the pairs and that the flat sides are together. If you are using Urac-185, work carefully in a room with as low a temperature as you can manage.

A wheel with lamb's wool buffer is used here to apply final glossy finish to the nock of the bow.

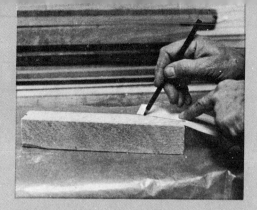

French curve would come in handy to mark curvature of handle riser, but other ways can be used.

If French curves are unavailable then cut your own patterns in reverse and use them for marking.

Finish the bow with series of coats of plastic-based elasticized varnish, to protect from wear.

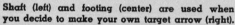

Shaft (left) and footing (center) are used when you decide to make your own target arrow (right).

Successive stages show how the gradual rounding of the shaft is done with planes and sandpaper.

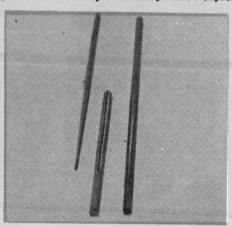

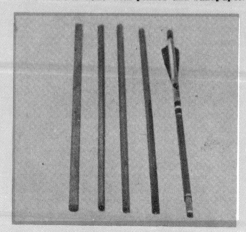

Being a heat-curing adhesive, the lower room temperature will give you more time to finish the work.

Once your glue is applied, thoroughly but not too thickly, cover your glass-lamination sandwich with more grease-proof paper. Over this lay a strip of rubber wrapping, 2″ wide and running slightly longer than your bow. Now take your battens and lay them along the surface, in the place of the more conventional pressure blocks.

Apply your clamps, working out along both limbs from the center and putting minimum pressure on at first. When all the clamps are in place go back to the handle and increase the pressure on each in turn. Don't attempt to tighten them beyond hand pressure since this will glue-starve your joinings.

Now set your bow aside in a warm, dry place. The ideal temperature is just above 80° and it should be maintained for at least five days. By that time the glue should have made a specific weld, but remember that Urac and other urea-based adhesives make a firmer bond as times passes.

The limbs of the bow should now be reduced according to the profile given here. The best method is to cut with a hack saw, the blade having been turned flat so as to give you a firm guide as you cut. Make the cut $\frac{1}{16}$″ wider than the profile and finish by rounding both back and face toward the core. During this process you should tiller the bow, as you would any other, remembering that if your laminations have been tapered correctly and your gluing-up done with equal pressures down along both limbs, the curves should need very little fixing.

Lay out the arrow rest on your handle riser, remembering that the view given here is from the back of the bow. Remove the wood with a draw shave and finish off with a file. The handle can then be covered with leather.

Nocks are cut with a file, rounding them in carefully so as to avoid any friction on the string. At the throat of the nocks, bring a groove down the back of the recurve so that the string will lie there when the bow is braced. Due to the working of these curves the string will not entirely clear them until the bow is nearly at full draw. It is vitally important that these nocks are exactly in the center of the recurves, since to off-center them in any way will cause twist and may easily ruin your bow.

This finished bow is designed to take a twenty-four inch arrow and will give you just about 45 pounds at full draw. You may want to overdraw it, to gain that extra few yards, but it is not a course that can be recommended. Far better to practice until you are sure that you are getting the maximum flight from your arrow before you experiment with overdrawing. A snapping or shattering bow is not only dangerous but it represents the waste of all your time and energy spent in making it.

Psychologically, too, careful handling is greatly to your advantage, because getting gradually used to your bow will imbue you with the confidence you need. •

Now comes the final part of making your arrow. It is finished by a careful sanding of the shaft. It calls for meticulous and time-consuming work, but it's still a pleasure to many archers who desire a set of matched arrows.

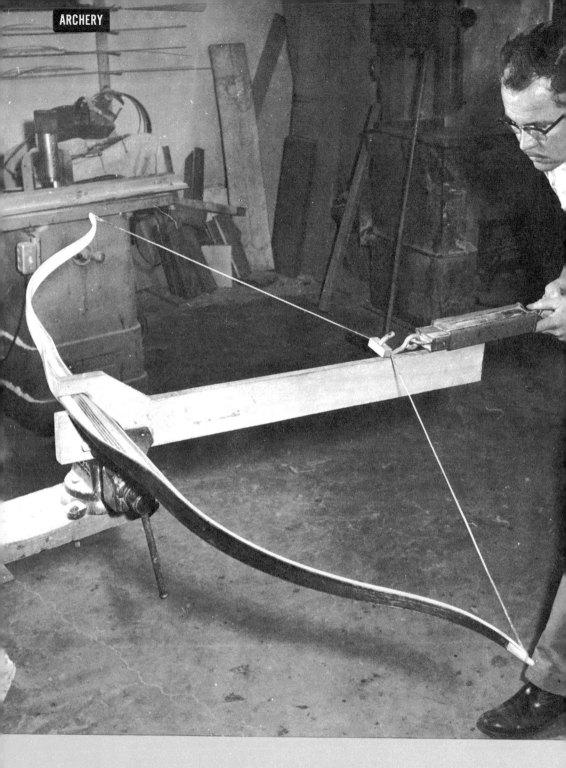

Tom Jennings of S. & J. Archery checks the weight of a finished laminated recurve bow with spring scale and graduated base board. Glass and core lamination thicknesses largely determine weight of each bow.

How to Make a Recurve Bow

The knowledge gained through the experience of making your own bow makes this more than just a prideful accomplishment.

SOONER or later the enthusiastic archer gets a yen to make his own bow. His reasons may be economical or experimental, but whatever they are, his skill as a craftsman should be equal to his enthusiasm or his venture into bow-making could prove dismal and costly. It's one thing to get a slat or stave of lemonwood and whittle out a simple bow that will perform to a fair degree of satisfaction, but the beginner who attempts to make a laminated recurve bow is tackling the most difficult project in the critical field of bow-making. There are so many variables and pitfalls in the construction of a laminated bow that to turn out a successful job on the first try is an achievement in itself. Yet, the thrill of accomplishment and the knowledge gained through this experience make it a worthwhile venture, even if it takes two tries to succeed.

Today's modern bow is made up of laminations of wood and Fiberglas, the wood serving as a neutral core or spacer between two laminations of Fiberglas. Actually, it is the Fiberglas that does the work of the bow, carrying 88 percent of the load while the wood core carries only 12 percent. As you increase the spacing between the two Fiberglas laminations by using a thicker core, you automatically increase the strength of the bow by the square. Thus, if you double the thickness of the core, you increase the weight of the bow four times. Since the thickness of the laminations is measured in thousandths of an inch, it is easy to see how just a few thousandths of an inch more thickness in the core can make a bow too heavy for your use.

There are several woods that are suitable for bow-making, among them hickory, Osage orange, yew and lemonwood. However, maple is the most common core wood used in glass-faced and backed bows because it is a consistently hard, dense wood, very straight-grained, and readily available in good clear grades. The beginner is wise to use maple rather than some of the other woods which are tricky to handle because of knots and twisty grain patterns.

To make things easier for the beginner, there is a bow kit available that con-

Core laminations are cut from same block of hard maple in order to insure matched limbs.

Kit contains all materials needed for making laminated recurve bow in weight desired.

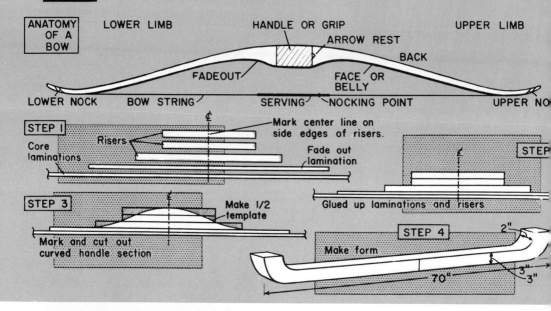

ANATOMY OF A BOW

LOWER LIMB   HANDLE OR GRIP   UPPER LIMB

ARROW REST

BACK

FADEOUT   FACE OR BELLY

LOWER NOCK   BOW STRING   SERVING   NOCKING POINT   UPPER NO

STEP 1
Core laminations   Risers   Mark center line on side edges of risers.
Fade out lamination

STEP

Glued up laminations and risers

STEP 3
Make 1/2 template
Mark and cut out curved handle section

STEP 4
Make form
2"
70"
3"
3"

Glue up risers and base core laminations; clamp unit to straight bar to insure good glue lines.

After glue has dried, clean off edges of bow assembly and lay out curve it is to be cut down to.

tains all the necessary woods, Fiberglas and glues to make a custom, 5-foot 6-inch recurve bow. The wood sections and Fiberglas strips are of uniform thickness and the wood is cut from matched sections of hard maple wood of the finest quality. The kit, which sells for $24.95, is put out by S. & J. Archery, 10945 Burbank Blvd., North Hollywood, Calif., makers of custom Smithwick bows, and provides all the necessary materials to make a custom bow, as shown in the photos in this chapter.

Before making a bow, however, it is a good idea to acquaint yourself with the anatomy of a bow and the terms used to denote its various parts. As shown in the diagram on this page, the bow, when held vertically, has an upper and lower limb, each extending from the central handle or grip. The smooth ledge cut into the upper part of the grip on the side where the arrow will travel is called the arrow rest or plate. The side of the bow facing away from the archer is called the back, while the side facing the archer is called the belly or face. The belly portions on either end of the handle that taper inward toward the limbs are called the fadeouts or dips. At the end of each limb is a string groove which is called the nock, known respectively as the upper and lower nock. The bowstring has a reinforced center section called the serving; the little ball of string located opposite the arrow plate and used

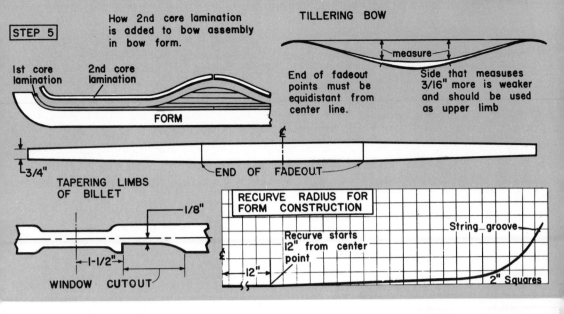

STEP 5

How 2nd core lamination is added to bow assembly in bow form.

1st core lamination   2nd core lamination

FORM

TILLERING BOW

measure

End of fadeout points must be equidistant from center line.

Side that measures 3/16" more is weaker and should be used as upper limb

3/4"

END OF FADEOUT

TAPERING LIMBS OF BILLET

1/8"

1-1/2"

WINDOW CUTOUT

RECURVE RADIUS FOR FORM CONSTRUCTION

Recurve starts 12" from center point

String groove

12"

2" Squares

to take the guesswork out of nocking the arrow is called the nocking point.

To make the custom bow shown in the photos, you will need the following materials, all of which are supplied in the bow kit mentioned above, and can be purchased as a unit or as separate items:

2 strips Fiberglas (1¾x36) ....for belly of bow
2 strips Fiberglas (1¾x36) ....for back of bow
4 lengths Canadian hard maple lamination (1¾x36)
....for core of bow
1 length maple lamination (1¾x28x¼) ....
.................base lamination to be faded into core
1 maple block (1¾x18x½) ....
.... for riser, or center section of bow
2 maple blocks (1¾x14x½) ....for top of riser
2 maple blocks (1½x¾x¼) ....
........................for string groove reinforcement
1 bottle M-74 plastic glue ....
.....................................for cementing glass to wood
1 bottle C-31 plastic hardener ......used on glass only
1 bottle Urac No. 185 ......for cementing wood to wood
1 bottle Urac hardener ....
....for all wood-to-wood surfaces

The thicknesses of the glass and core laminations determine to a large extent the weight of the finished bow and should be carefully selected with that in mind. It is practically impossible to draw up a formula that will give you the correct thicknesses for any specific weight bow because of the many other factors that can affect your bow weight. For instance, your bow weight will be affected also by the length of the bow, the design and amount of recurve, its width and taper, and the type wood used in the core. A long center-section riser

Use a band saw or jig saw to cut out this curve, taking care not to cut into fade-out lamination.

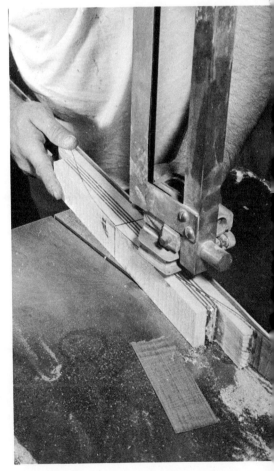

will shorten the working limbs and increase the weight of the bow, while a shorter grip section will allow you longer working limbs and thus lighten the bow. It takes very little to add or subtract 10 pounds from the weight of a bow and, for this reason, anyone building a laminated bow of his own design can never be sure what weight it will be until he can actually test the bow.

Bow makers make many bows and do a considerable amount of experimenting before they establish a standard of operation for any one bow, and because this has been done with the Smithwick Custom Bow, it is possible to order a bow kit for the weight bow you wish to make. The kit will then have laminations of the correct thickness to give you the right basis from which to start. Even then, the success of your ultimate weight goal will depend on how skillfully you shape and taper the limbs. Once the billet or roughed-out bow is completed, you cannot add any more weight to it. You can only take weight off.

As a general rule, the following lamination thickness specifications will, if applied to the bow design shown, produce a bow that will correspond closely to the desired weight you wish to achieve: for a 50 lb. bow: .175-inch core, .050-inch back glass and .060-inch belly glass; for a 40 lb. bow: .175-inch core, .042-inch back glass and .048-inch belly glass; for a 25-30 lb. bow: .160-inch core, .040-inch back glass and .045-inch belly glass.

The lighter 25-30 lb. bow is usually a lady's bow and requires additional changes in the tapering of the billet to bring the weight down without reducing the thickness of the limbs too much. This is because there is a ratio between the thickness and the width of the limbs where the bow gives the best performance.

With all your materials laid out, you are now ready for the first step in making your bow. This step consists of gluing the riser blocks to the core laminations. However, before applying any glue, it is a good idea to assemble the component parts dry and familiarize yourself with the position each piece occupies so that there will be no mistakes when the glue is applied. Once the glue has been applied, you must join and clamp the pieces together without delay in order to get a perfect bond. To make sure that the pieces are positioned properly, mark the center line across the side edge of each piece. When all units are assembled, the center lines should coincide to form a straight line across the edge of the risers.

In this first step, you glue together only the three riser blocks, the fade-out lamination, and one pair of core laminations. The pair of core laminations are laid end to end under the riser blocks to form a continuous 6-foot long core as shown in the diagram. This core comes in two sections; in order to assure perfectly matched upper and lower limbs, two 36-inch lengths of core lamination are cut from the same 36-

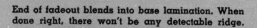

Taper fadeout into base lamination. Extreme care must be taken to avoid gouging base lamination.

End of fadeout blends into base lamination. When done right, there won't be any detectable ridge.

Glue second pair of core laminations, Fiberglas facings to bow assembly and secure to bow form.

Inner-tube strips or tape can be used to secure assembly to bow form to establish recurve shape.

inch long block of hard maple. The two pieces, coming from the same section of wood, are as closely matched in grain and wood characteristics as is possible to achieve. This is true also of the second pair of core laminations which are glued to the assembly in another operation.

The wood portions can be cemented together with any good wood glue, such as urea-base glues or Elmer's Glue. The glue supplied with the kit is Urac No. 185, which is used with a Urac hardener. Apply the glue evenly with a 1½-inch brush to both surfaces being joined and clamp the assembly firmly between blocks and a straight bar of wood or metal. The straight bar is important for insuring good glue lines. Use enough clamps to distribute the pressure evenly along the entire area being

Glued bow assembly is clamped to steel form and dried in heating chamber in professional set-up.

Howard Hill dries his bows with heat of a blow torch directed into improvised drying chamber.

glued. Allow 24 hours drying time, the first six hours at at least 100 degrees Fahrenheit. A closed car in the summer sun will usually get at least this hot. Another trick is to wrap the glued assembly in a sheet of canvas that has been treated for water-proofing and let this lie in the direct sun. The heat will build up in the canvas wrapping to a very high degree. Howard Hill improvises a drying chamber by wrapping a length of 10-inch stovepipe with asbestos, closing it off at both ends, but leaving a small enough opening at one end through which to direct the heat of a blowtorch.

While the assembly is drying, make a wooden form for shaping the billet. This form should be bandsawed out of a 2-inch thick solid wood block that is seven inches wide and 70 inches long. In the absence of solid wood, plywood can be used by lam-inating two lengths of ¾-inch and one length of ½-inch plywood together to build up the 2-inch thickness required. Cut the form out to the shape shown in the diagram, making sure that both ends of the form cut out are identical in shape. The best way to assure this is to make a template, from heavy cardboard or thin sheet metal, of one half of the desired shape, then trace this onto the form block, first on one end of the block and then, flopped, on the other end of the block. The form, when cut out, should be perfectly square to insure a firm even base for clamping the glued lamina-tions. After cutting out the recurve con-tour, draw a line on the form parallel to

After drying by heat at recommended temperature, bindings are taken off and billet is removed from form. Billet will have taken recurve shape. Clean and square up both sides of the billet by sanding.

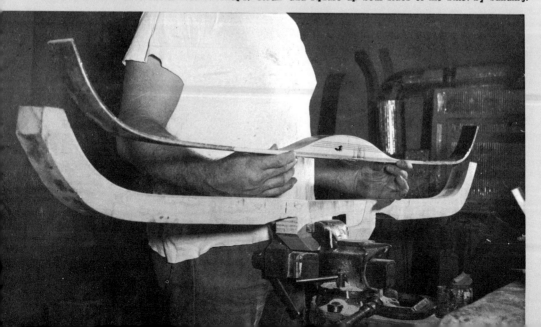

this shape and spaced three inches from it and cut away the excess wood along this line. The precision and evenness with which you make this form will determine the quality of your finished bow to a great degree.

After the bow assembly has dried, clean the excess glue off both sides of the riser section and then lay out the curve it is to be cut down to as shown in diagram (Step No. 3). Since both sides of the riser section fadeouts are the same shape and equally distant from the center line, a half template can be used in both positions to trace the curve onto the riser section. The fadeout *must* be a very gradual curve into the base or core lamination. This is essential to the final tiller of the bow.

Use a band saw or jig saw to cut out this curve but do not cut into the fade-out lamination. The gradation of the fadeout is too critical an operation to be done with a saw. It should be done by careful sanding, preferably using a drum sander, until the fadeout gradually blends into the core lamination. Be very careful not to cut *into* the core lamination or leave even the slightest ridge at the end of the fadeout. Cutting into the core lamination will weaken the bow at that point, while leaving a ridge will stiffen the limb, add to the bow's weight, and interfere with the bow's performance.

The next step is to glue the second pair of core laminations to the bow assembly. This operation is performed in the bow form in order to establish the recurve shape. The

Cover outer Fiberglas surfaces with masking tape for protection and to facilitate marking layout.

Using a flexible tape measure or rule, establish the center of the bow, taking care to be precise.

Now draw two center lines on the bow, one crosswise and the other lengthwise. All measurements should be very carefully made as even a slight error will be reflected in the accuracy of the finished bow.

Measure exact distance from center to end of either fadeout. Mark off equal distance other limb.

Mark off bow tips for required width, then lay out limb tapers from end of fadeout to bow tip.

best way to do this is to set the two strips end to end and secure them together temporarily with masking tape across their outer surfaces. Then apply glue to the inner surfaces of both strips and the back surface of the bow assembly. Now join the laminations together, centering the taped joint with the center line on the riser section and lining it up with the center line on the bow form. Do this in the form, using a C-clamp on the center line to clamp the assembly to the form. Then, starting at the center point and using loops cut from an old inner tube, numerous clamps or masking tape, secure the laminations firmly to the form. To facilitate removal of the billet from the form, wax paper should be placed between the form and the laminations. Also, because the rubber loops and tape, when tightly wound around the assembly, exert most of the pressure on the edges of the laminations and very little in the middle, a spacer strip, consisting of a strip of wood $\frac{1}{16}$ inch thick and $\frac{1}{8}$ inch narrower than the laminations, should be laid along the top of the billet and centered to leave a $\frac{1}{16}$-inch margin along each side before the tape or rubber

loops are wound around the assembly. This spacer strip will equalize the pressure exerted over the entire surface and insure a good glue line. No glue is applied to this spacer strip.

As you work your way toward the bow tips, the laminations will be forced down into the form and will take the shape of the curve cut into the form. Do this along both ends, securing the entire length, then set the form into a hot place to dry. Because extreme heat may melt natural rubber, loops preferably should be cut from one of the synthetic-type tubes which are more heat resistant. Dry the billet at no less than 100 degrees F. When the glue dries, the laminations will retain the shape of the form. Clean off the excess glue from the sides of the core and, with No. ½ grit sandpaper, clean off any wax that might have transferred to the core from the wax paper.

The next step is to apply the Fiberglas to the bow assembly. The Fiberglas is obtained in two thicknesses, the heavier strips being used on the belly of the bow and the lighter ones on the back. Rough the sides of the glass to be glued (either side can be

Cut away the excess limb. Clean and face the edges up to the layout lines, rounding Fiberglas slightly with a mill file.

Having determined which is to be the upper limb and which the lower, lay out the handle and sight window and cut to shape.

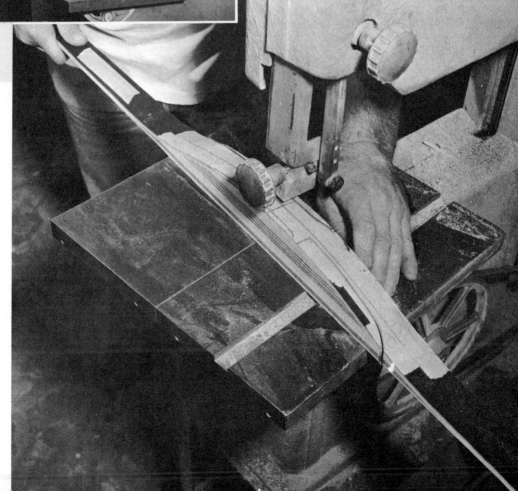

Following the photos on these pages, rough shape the bow handle, on a disc sander if you have one.

Curve top surface of the arrow rest slightly so that shaft does not rest on too broad a surface.

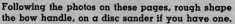

used) with very coarse sandpaper, preferably using a drum sander, to remove all the glaze. Do not be afraid to sand.

Next, join the two strips of back glass end to end with masking tape applied to the side opposite the one roughed up for gluing and lay this glass, rough side up, into the form. The wooden bow assembly then sets in on this, and the belly glass, joined end to end with masking tape like the back glass, is set on top of the whole assembly. This is a "dry run" to make sure that all the component parts are properly sanded and ready for gluing. It is a good idea to cover the outer surfaces of both the back and belly glass with masking tape. The tape will keep the glass clean and provide a surface for measuring and marking off the limb tapers to be cut later.

Now, using M-74 plastic glue and C-31 hardener, apply glue to the roughened glass surfaces first, then to both sides of the wood core, using a 1½-inch brush. Plastic glue and hardener should be applied *immediately* after they are mixed. The glue is mixed four parts adhesive to one part hardener by weight. Add the hardener to the resin and stir for five minutes. The maximum time you can allow the mixed glue to set in the pot is five to 10 minutes.

However, once it is spread on the laminations and glass, you have 30 minutes to join and clamp the pieces together. Glue surfaces must be absolutely free of moisture.

After you've glued the surfaces, set them into the form with a spacer strip laid across the top as was done when gluing the second pair of laminations to the first, and after lining up the center mark with the one on the form, use a C-clamp over the center mark to hold the assembly to the form. Then, as was done before, wrap the billet tightly to the form with loops of inner-tube rubber or masking tape, starting from the center point and working your way toward the tips. The glass will take the shape of the curved form as you carry the wrappings outward. Be sure to save some of the plastic glue and hardener (in unmixed form) for the tip blocks. Dry the billet with heat of at least 120 degrees F., but not over 140 degrees, for six hours, then let harden for another 48 hours. Important: this glue will not function properly without observing the stated degree of temperature.

You now have the completed billet. Clean and square up both sides of the billet with very coarse sandpaper, using your disc sander. Leave the masking tape on the bow for use in marking the layout. Now draw

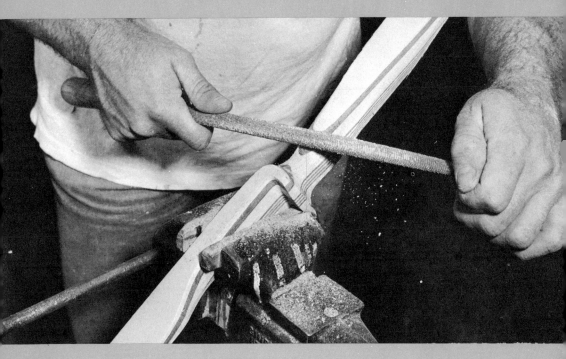

Final shaping is done with files. You can shape the sighting window to your own requirements, there being no hard rules concerning the location of the window or the depth to which is should be cut.

two center lines on the bow, one lengthwise and the other crosswise. From the crosswise center line, measure the distance to the exact end of the fadeout on one side and draw another crossline at this point. Then measure an equal distance on the other side of the center line and draw another line across the bow belly. These lines at the ends of the fadeout will mark the points from which the bow limbs begin to taper toward the tips.

Next, at the tips of the bow, measure ⅜ inch from each side of the longitudinal center line. This will give you ¾-inch wide bow tips. Now draw diagonal lines from these bow tip marks to the outer ends of the fadeout cross lines and you will have the correct limb taper as shown in diagram. For a 25 to 30 lb. lady's bow, the billet, which is normally 1⅝ inches wide, should be narrowed down on a disc sander to a width of 1½ inches and the limb taper should end up with ⅝-inch-wide tips instead of ¾-inch.

After marking off the limb tapers, cut away the excess limb along these lines and then clean and face the edges up to the layout lines. Round the glass slightly on the face and back with a mill file, but do not go to too much trouble because these limbs

are rough width at the tips and will be changed when the bow is lined up.

Next, locate the points for the string grooves by measuring 33 inches each way from the center line with a flexible tape or rule, letting the rule follow the curve of the bow along the belly. Use a small round rat-tail file and file the string grooves ⅛ inch deep on both sides of the tip, rounding them off slightly to prevent their cutting the tillering string.

You are now ready to string the bow for tillering. The tiller is the shape of the bow at strung position. Use a string with large loops for the tillering string. After stringing up the bow, check its limbs for evenness by sighting along the string from tip to the middle of the main part of the limb as shown in photo. If the recurve twists to one side of the middle of the limb, remove material on that side and refile the string groove on that side. Repeat this process until the recurve is in the middle of the main part of the bow.

After the tips are in line, sight along each side of the limb and file out any bumps you may see. In doing this, you may change the tiller of the bow, so check frequently to see that the recurves do not take on an off-side twist. If they do, you can correct it by tak-

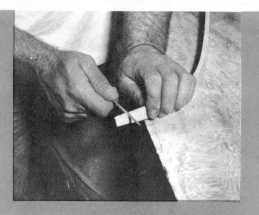

String grooves, ⅛ inch deep, are filed into both sides of each bow tip using small rat-tail file.

Glue tip blocks to bow tips over string grooves; Fiberglas should be well roughened before gluing.

Shape bow tips to the contour of the bow limbs. File string grooves into tips with rat-tail file.

Finishing off the bow, file string grooves along the recurve on belly side of each of the limbs.

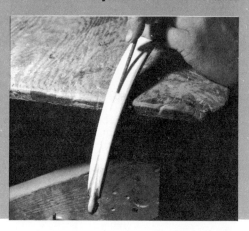

ing off sufficient material from the side to which the limb twists to even out the limb.

Before the handle can be shaped out, you must determine which limb will be the upper limb, since the upper limb should be weaker than the lower limb. This is because when drawing the bow, you will be exerting more palm pressure below the center line on your grip, as well as putting more tension on the lower half of the bow string due to having two fingers below the nock of the arrow and only one above it. To equalize this, the lower limb of the bow should be a little stiffer than the upper limb, and you determine this by measuring the distance between the bow string and the limb curve at the point of the fadeout on both limbs. The points along the limbs at which you take this measure should be equidistant from the center line of the bow. The weaker limb should then measure $\frac{3}{16}$ inch more between limb face and string than the stronger limb and this limb should be used as the upper limb. If it measures less than $\frac{3}{16}$ inch, you can lighten the limb by rounding the face glass slightly.

Having tillered the bow and determined which is to be the upper limb, you can now mark the handle for the grip and window cutout as shown in diagram, lining it up so that the window cutout is on the upper limb. Cut out the handle as shown in photos with files and disc sander; round out the handle and sight window to the desired shape as shown in diagram. You can shape this to your own taste, there being no hard and fast rules concerning the location of the sight window and the depth to which it

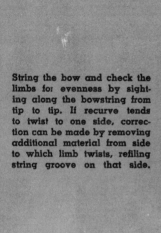

String the bow and check the limbs for evenness by sighting along the bowstring from tip to tip. If recurve tends to twist to one side, correction can be made by removing additional material from side to which limb twists, refiling string groove on that side.

should be cut. However, it should not be cut to a depth greater than ⅛ inch from the longitudinal center line as shown. This sight window should be cut on the left side of the bow (as bow is seen by archer when shooting) for right-handed shooters, on the opposite side from that shown in the diagram for left-handed shooters. File a slight curve into the top surface of the arrow rest so that the shaft does not rest on too broad a surface when shooting.

Finally, cement the tip blocks to the bow tips over the string grooves. Finish off the tips by shaping them down to the contour of the bow limbs and filing the string grooves into them with a rat-tail file.

Your bow is now ready for sanding and painting. Sand to a fine smoothness and paint with clear varnish or lacquer.

SOME FINAL TIPS:

1. When removing masking tape, strip from center of bow out toward tips so as not to lift any glass splinters along the edges. Use care.

2. When filing bow, always file toward glass to avoid chipping.

3. Before any clamping, always have a "dry run" before applying glue.

4. Remember, you must use heat to cure this glue right.

5. Glass surfaces to be glued must be roughed thoroughly.

6. Extreme care should be used in fadeout to avoid gouging base lamination or have fadeout end too abruptly.

7. Do not get impatient to shoot bow before it is finished. •

Constructing A 6 Inch Reflector

Photos by George Tilton

The most popular amateur telescope, versatile 6-inch reflector is both portable and quite easy to use.

THE 6-inch f/8 Newtonian reflecting telescope is probably the most popular star gazing instrument in use by amateur astronomers. This is easily understood when we examine the instrument in more detail.

The "6-inch" refers to the diameter of the objective or main mirror of the telescope and thus affects the diameter of the main telescope tube. The figure "f/8" is an optical expression derived from the ratio between the focal length and the diameter of the telescope mirror. In this case, the focal length is 48 inches or 8 times the mirror diameter of 6 inches.

The name "Newtonian" refers to the over-all design of this type of reflecting telescope in which rays from the objective or main mirror are focused onto a smaller mirror known as the "diagonal." The diagonal is set further up in the telescope tube at a 45° angle to the main mirror and the eyepiece. Its function is to reflect the focused rays from the objective into the eyepiece where they are refocused and magnified for close viewing of the image.

It is enough to say that the Newtonian design is simply the most practical and least expensive for nonprofessional instruments. The word "reflecting," of course, distinguishes this scope from a *refractor* in which the light rays are "bent" through and focused behind a lens instead of being "bounced" away from and focused in front of a mirror.

Since the above description pretty well fixes the size of our reflector we can see one reason for its popularity. It's about the largest telescope you can comfortably carry. Larger reflecting instruments—up to 8 inches in diameter—are almost always semiportable, with usually a permanent mount and perhaps a transportable main tube. Much larger reflectors—those over 8 inches in mirror diameter—require the construction of a permanent observatory.

Another obvious reason for the popularity of Newtonian reflectors this size or smaller is price. To buy a completely finished and assembled 6-inch reflector of

Back view of mirror mount shows tension bolts for adjusting tilt. Clips hold mirror in the mount.

Mirror is mounted tight in holding ring; add shims at edges if needed. Attach retaining clips.

Courtesy Edmund Scientific Co.

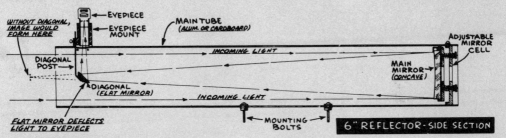

6" REFLECTOR - SIDE SECTION

SIX-INCH REFLECTOR — $150

(as illustrated in this chapter — includes finished mirror and mount)

Pyrex Parabolic 6" Mirror	$59.50
6" Mirror Mount	7.50
7" O.D. Aluminum Tube	15.00
Eyepiece Mount	8.50
Elliptical Mirror Diagonal	3.75
Mirror Diagonal Holder	1.00
Equatorial Mount and Tripod	39.50
Kellner Eyepiece 28 mm F.L.	7.95
6-Power Finder Scope, Bracket	8.00

(Above prices are quoted by Edmund Scientific Co., Barrington, New Jersey)

SIX-INCH REFLECTOR — $27

(Economy Kit—with unground mirror blank, and minus telescope mount)

6" Mirror Kit with Eyepiece-lenses and mirror diagonal	$11.95
6" Mirror Mount	7.50
7⅜" O.D. Cardboard Tube	4.00
Eyepiece Tubing	.50
Eyepiece Mount	2.50
Diagonal Holder	1.00

(Above prices are quoted by Edmund Scientific Co., Barrington, New Jersey)

this type would cost you about $200. Prices of larger instruments soar drastically for the finished product. You can, however, own a high quality instrument for a fraction of the price if you build or assemble your own telescope. The object of this chapter is to help you do just that.

REFLECTOR TELESCOPE KITS—You will note that there are two lists of parts printed on these pages. There is an

economy kit of parts for around $27 and another kit, illustrated here, for $150. Why the large difference? Primarily, it is the difference between buying a finished parabolic mirror and grinding your own. Grinding astronomical mirrors is a fascinating hobby in itself. It does, however, require a healthy degree of skill and patience. We have chosen, therefore, to illustrate the assembly of scope parts that requires only the use of simple hand tools and a minimum of time. If you elect to grind your own mirror, the telescope assembly instructions shown here will still apply.

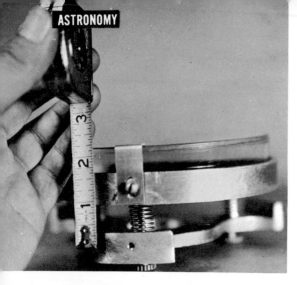

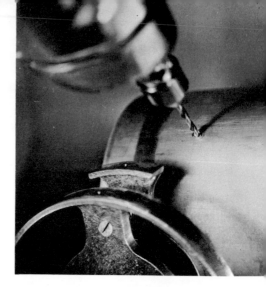

Measure distance from mounting hole to mirror surface then store the mirror until final assembly.

Drill mirror mount holes 1-2″ from end of main tube. Mirror must be mounted squarely in the tube.

Check exact FL of mirror and subtract sum of "A" and "B" (see text) to find the eyepiece location.

Eyepiece must be located exactly by measuring from point representing front surface of mirror.

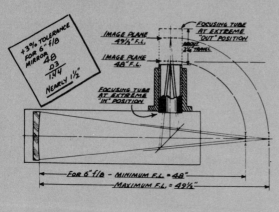

Courtesy Edmund Scientific Co.

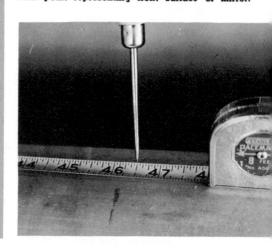
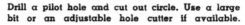

Draw a circle with diameter barely larger than diameter of the traveling eyepiece tube in mount.

Drill a pilot hole and cut out circle. Use a large bit or an adjustable hole cutter if available.

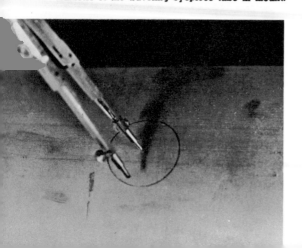

Another price factor is the inclusion of a good equatorial mount. You can build your own simple mount or purchase a less expensive altazimuth mount. But we highly recommend an equatorial mount for the serious star gazer. As you become more and more advanced in the science of astronomy, you will need an equatorial mount and you can save a considerable amount of money if you purchase one at the start.

With an equatorial mount you can use setting circles—accessories that allow you to "dial" the exact sky object you want to see by checking its location in a star atlas. A clock drive—essential for any type of astrophotography more complicated than snapping a picture of the moon —also requires an equatorial mount.

Having acquired your telescope parts, you are ready to go to work. First, let's examine our assemblage of optical equipment.

Basically, we have a big mirror and its mount that will occupy the lower end of a large aluminum tube and a small mirror and eyepiece holder that will occupy the upper end. The correct placement of these parts in the tube is our only major assembly problem and the key to this problem is the focal length of the main mirror.

Our large mirror, being concave, will converge light rays from the sky to a point in front of it—the focal point. A small, concentrated image will form at this point, which your eyepiece, in turn, will enlarge to the view you see when you actually observe the heavens. The small diagonal

Mousetail hack saw blade with pistol grip can be used to cut hole. Aluminum is easy to work.

After rough cutting, smooth to perfect circle with semiround file. Check with the eyepiece tube.

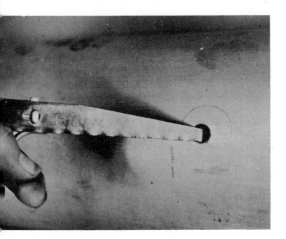

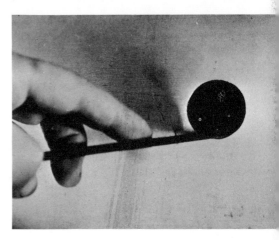

Circle is notched for rack on eyepiece tube and holes are drilled for bolts holding the mount.

Finished cutout for eyepiece mount. The hole at middle left is for the diagonal mirror holder.

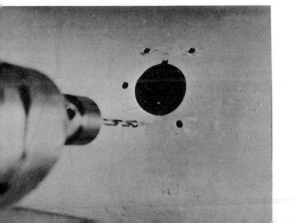

Check fit of eyepiece mount to holes drilled. Make any corrections before painting the main tube.

Diagonal mirror is cemented to holder while protected by tissue. Use a strong glue like epoxy.

Completed diagonal mirror cemented to holder is shown below. Next step is to insert in mount.

Diagonal mirror holder extends through rack and is held in place by a set screw on eyepiece mount.

Next step is to drill holes in scope tube to secure it to the carriage of the equatorial mount.

mirror catches the image at this point and reflects it into the eyepiece tube. To do this, the focal point must be placed just outside the eyepiece tube of the eyepiece mount when this tube is at its furthest "in" position. The reason for this location is that eyepieces, having their own focal points of varying lengths, must have room to focus on the image or focal point formed by the big mirror. A short focal length (high power) eyepiece will focus close to this "in" position, but longer focal length (low power) eyepieces will need more "out" travel and will focus when the eyepiece tube is extended to nearly its full length or furthest "out" position.

Now we know where we want the focal point of the main mirror but have to figure out how to get it there. Before proceeding, it should be mentioned that manufactured mirrors may vary slightly in focal length from the given figure. A tolerance of about

an inch and a half is generally allowed. A 48-inch focal length mirror may actually be of 49½-inch f.l., therefore. A small sticker on the back of the mirror usually gives the exact figure, *which you should check carefully.* The main tube should be slightly longer than this focal length. We used a 5-foot tube, but this could have been cut to 50 inches.

BEFORE DRILLING into your tube, place the main mirror in its mount. Now measure the distance from any one mounting hole on the mirror-mount to the front edge of the mirror. Jot this figure down for future reference. You may now put your mirror away in a safe place as you will not need it

Although the location of the finder scope is not critical, it must be parallel to the main tube.

Locate and drill holes for finder bracket at point out of the way of the main scope eyepiece.

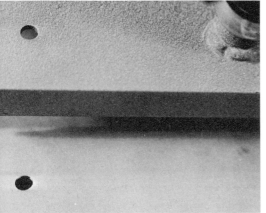

Line up mount and tube holes. Mount must be on side of tube opposite eyepiece for best viewing.

Main tube is tightly attached to the head of equatorial mount using ⅜" dia., 2" stove bolts.

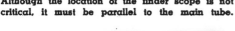

Bracket for the finder is shown with mounting bolts. Three set screws permit finder adjustment.

Finder telescope is simply slipped into mounting bracket and adjusted for the best operation.

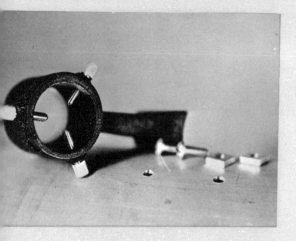

Equatorial mount (parts shown below) is better for observing than an altazimuth or other type.

A sturdy tripod is absolutely essential for observing; vibration makes any viewing impossible.

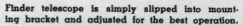

Adjusting knob on legs of tripod makes it possible to level the head on a variety of terrain.

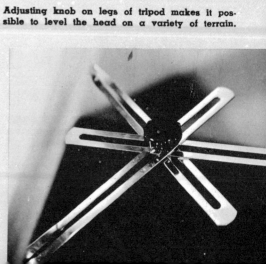

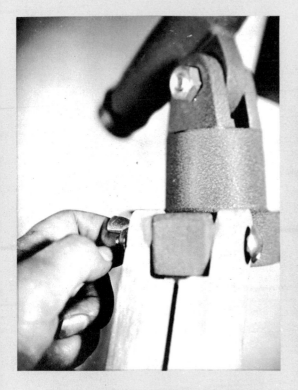

The equatorial mount is bolted to tripod. It permits scope to be set parallel to the earth's axis.

Completed equatorial mount looks like this. The scope carriage must be parallel to polar axis.

Polar axis must be set for latitude of observer. Check the mount head to see that it is level first.

Set a protractor at your local angle of latitude and clamp it to an ordinary carpenter's level.

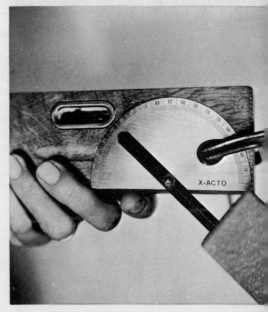

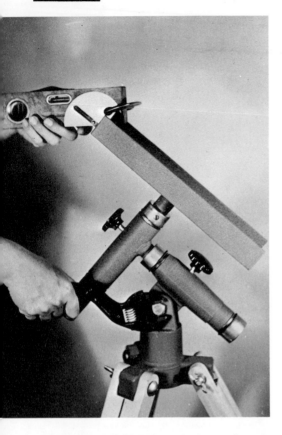

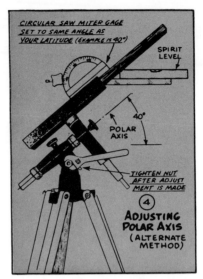

CIRCULAR SAW MITER GAGE
SET TO SAME ANGLE AS
YOUR LATITUDE (EXAMPLE IS 40°)

SPIRIT
LEVEL

40°

POLAR
AXIS

TIGHTEN NUT
AFTER ADJUST
MENT IS MADE

④ ADJUSTING
POLAR AXIS
(ALTERNATE
METHOD)

Courtesy Edmund Scientific Co.

After painting, mount scope on carriage with
strong bolts. Use washers and tighten bolts evenly.

Check your latitude before adjusting polar axis
as shown here and in the diagram at the right.

After adjustment, balancing weights are attached
to the declination axis shaft on the equatorial.

Completed equatorial mount on tripod with scope
attached gives sturdy platform for best viewing.

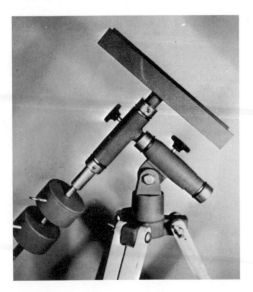

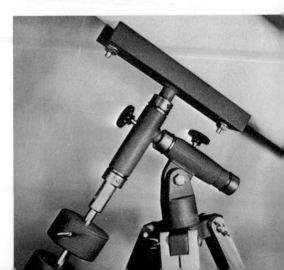

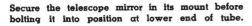

Secure the telescope mirror in its mount before bolting it into position at lower end of tube.

Attach the eyepiece holder to the tube. From inside the tube, next insert the diagonal mirror.

again until ready for the final assembly.

Next, drill the holes in the big tube that will hold your mirror-mount. The exact distance from the lower end of the tube is not critical; one of two inches is sufficient. *It is essential, however, that the mirror sits squarely in the tube.* Now, from any one of these mounting holes, measure along the tube the distance you have jotted down. *Mark this point with great care.* It shows you the position the front surface of your main mirror will occupy within the tube and *it is the point from which you will measure to locate the position of your eyepiece mount.*

Now for some simple, but vital, arithmetic. Measure the outside diameter of your main tube (in this case, 7 inches) and divide by 2. Let's call this figure "A." Next, place the rack-and-pinion eyepiece mount on the exterior of the main tube and measure the distance from the surface of the main tube to a point about a quarter of an inch above the end of the eyepiece tube at its fullest "in" position. Let's call this measured number figure "B." Add figure "A" and figure "B." Then subtract the sum of these two figures from the focal length of your main mirror. That's the end of your arithmetic. Take the final figure and measure along your main tube from the point you jotted down and marked with such great care as described in the preceding paragraph. This point is the exact center of a circular hole you will cut out of the main tube to receive the moving tube of your eyepiece rack-and-pinion mount.

Read all of the above paragraph over before doing any of the work on your telescope tube. *It is the most critical step in the whole assembly of your instrument.*

Further assembly is relatively simple and can be done by closely following the step-by-step photographs. Here are a few pointers:

Remember that when drilling holes to attach the main tube to the equatorial mount that these holes should be on just the opposite side of the main tube from the eyepiece rack-and-pinion mount holes. This will give you the most comfortable position when observing with your eyepieces for most sections of the sky. You may center the main tube on the carriage of your equatorial mount or find a more delicate balance by assembling all optical parts and locating a fulcrum where the entire assembly balances.

Remember to level the head of the equatorial mount before setting the polar axis to an angle equal to your own latitude.

Paint the exterior of your scope any color *but the interior color must be the flattest optical black possible.* Exterior is perhaps most often a clear white, which is easiest to see on a dark night.

Collimation of your optical system when completely assembled can be done in a variety of ways. Sketches in this chapter show a simple, effective method.

Weights on the declination axis of the equatorial mount may be adjusted to balance the main tube assembly so that it swings freely on the polar axis. •

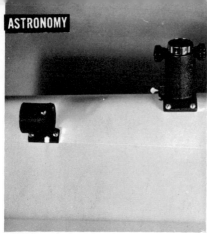

Photo shows one possible location for finder where it won't interfere with operation of regular eyepiece. Finder bracket is left, the eyepiece at right.

Finder scope is inserted in place parallel to main scope tube as shown here. Finder is centered with the main scope optics by means of the three setscrews shown.

Final step in adjusting the telescope finder is to focus it on an object at infinity. The finder is indispensable in aiming the main scope for observation purposes.

The small diagonal mirror must be exactly centered in the main tube. Follow the sketch (right).

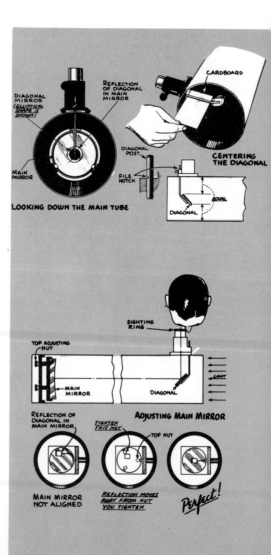

Adjust tension screws to center main mirror. Reflection of the diagonal serves as a guide (right).

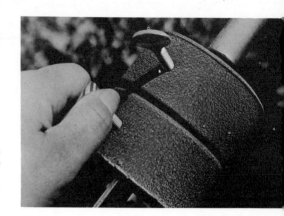

Final steps include insertion of eyepiece (above) and adjustment of counterbalance weights (right) to offset weight of main tube and optics. Entire assembly should swing freely on the polar axis.

Finished high-quality 6-inch reflector looks like this. In addition to being a popular instrument for the serious observer, scope can be used for astrophotography with addition of clock drive and camera assembly.

a 3-inch refractor for $75

Here is a fine portable and easily stored telescope that can be built for half of its commercial cost.

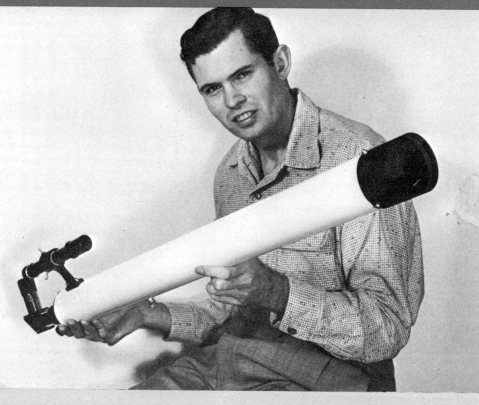

Completed refractor is displayed here by Optical Expert Jack Wegener, who constructed it for photographer.

WHILE there are certain predominant qualities of both of the basic telescope types—reflector and refractor—that give one an advantage over the other in each of several special kinds of work, it remains an obvious fact that for the person who has limited storage space, who travels frequently or who cannot give as much time as he would like to astronomical observations, the refractor is *the* telescope.

It is much more portable and requires less care. Enclosed in a sealed metal tube, the refractor practically eliminates for its owner those irksome problems inspired by dust and moisture. This does not mean, of course, that its owner can be careless about the outer surfaces of lenses. A disadvantage of the refractor is that—size-for-size, comparatively—it is much more expensive than a reflector.

The refractor described on these pages normally sells for $125 and higher—depending on the quality of the objective lenses. Its useful objective diameter of almost three inches brings within its range the polar "ice" caps of Mars, the bands and spots of Jupiter as well as that planet's moons, the rings of Saturn and at least five of her nine moons, Uranus and Neptune and a big variety of nebulae—as well as that old standby: the craters and mountains of the Moon. •

MATERIALS-COST LIST

3-inch color corrected, air-spaced achromats, mounted in cell	$42.95
3-inch o.d. aluminum tubing, 48 inches long	6.00
Refractor rack and pinion eyepiece mount	12.95
Finder	8.00
Miscellany (cardboard, black paper, screws, bolts, etc.)	.25
	$70.15

These prices are quoted by Edmund Scientific Co. Barrington, N. J. No eyepiece is included. Recommended are 28 mm focal length Kellner, $7.95. Alternate recommendations are the 1/2-inch Ramsden at $4.50; and 1/4-inch Ramsden at $4.75

All photos in this chapter are by Ed Pryor, with cooperation of Edmund Scientific Company

Below are basic parts of scope. Moving from left, clockwise, they are refractor rack-and-pinion eyepiece mount, hardware, paper lens-stops, black construction-paper, cardboard tubes for stops, aluminum tubing, black felt paper, eyepiece, finder and mount, 1 of 2 achromatic lenses and lens cell.

Diagram courtesy of Hayden Planetarium, American Museum of Natural History

Diagram shows in simplified way how light is refracted through objective lenses: it comes in scattered, is then bent straight.

Lens-stops are of extreme importance in refractor, are cut from black paper after tracing size with compass.

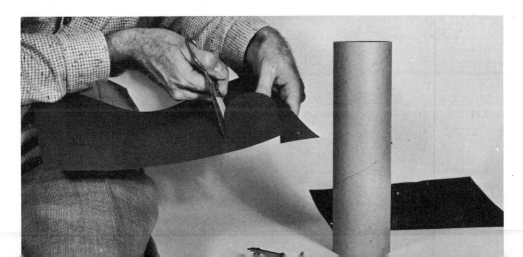

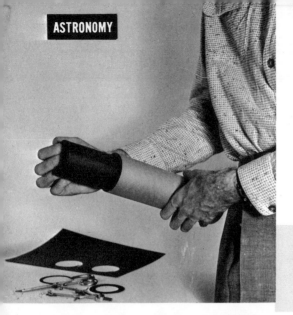

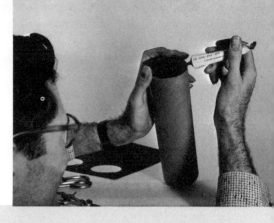

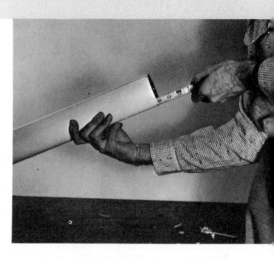

Here, stop is being set in place. Stops are used at both ends of first tube, one or both ends of a second (study diagram across bottom of this page).

Lens-stops are cemented onto ends of cardboard tube, but first tube is deadened inside with black felt paper, which also is cemented and smoothed.

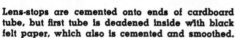

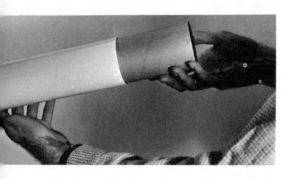

First lens-stop tube is slid into metal tube of telescope: cardboard tubes must be just the right diameter to fit snugly, can be bought for few cents.

Measure distance to approximate center of inner stop-tube with long rule: hold scope-tube toward light, then peer inside and mark point on outside.

Diagram here shows position of stops and way cone of light is focused by lenses. Stops are required so that light is not dissipated away from cone and doesn't scatter before entering eyepiece, thus dimming the image. Most important stop is No. 2 at scope-tube middle: hole-diameter must be 2 in. Stop in front of it (No. 1) is 2⅝ in. diameter and stop No. 3 is 1⅜ in. diameter. Cut these stop-holes carefully with a razor.

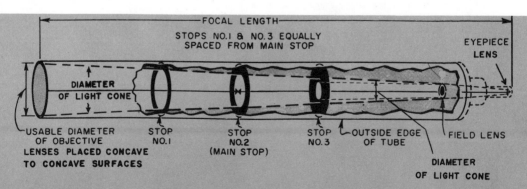

Hole is drilled at marked point in aluminum tube, right through cardboard tube. Notch a strip of wood (or bend heavy wire into loop) to hold machine-screw, which is then guided from inside tube and inserted in hole. Nut is then tightened from outside. Whole process is repeated with the second cardboard stop-tube.

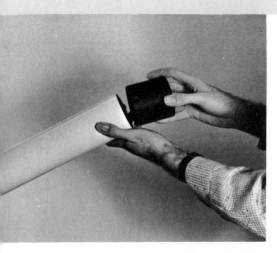
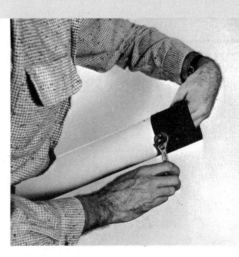

Long screws (1½ in.) should be used on previous steps, since screws will also serve to mount the telescope on tripod-head. But now attach lens-cell.

Holes are first drilled in lens-cell casing and aluminum scope-tube, then casing is made tight at front end of scope, using a wrench as shown above.

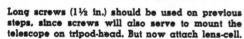

Now comes a tricky part of operation. Objective lenses must face concave-surface to convex. Slide one gently over other: right way creates suction.

Edges of lenses are often marked with arrows: these should point toward each other. Next, 3 small squares of black paper are spaced around lens.

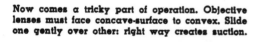

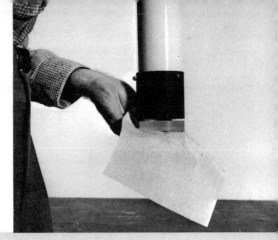

Separators provide air pocket between lenses. Place second lens carefully over one with separators. Both lenses should be resting on heavy tissue.

Lenses are then very carefully scooped up by sliding hand under tissue cloth. With other hand, lower cell casing evenly and gently over lenses.

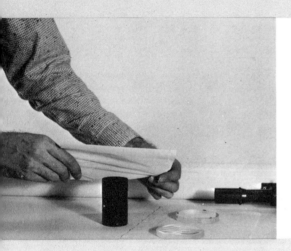

Another way to get lenses into cell is like this: using tin can or any sturdy cylinder as base, cover the cylinder with clean handkerchief, tissue.

Place lens with separators in place on tissue or handkerchief. Then place other lens on top. Be sure that "flint" lens is on top. It is thickest.

Then steadying telescope-tube with both hands, lower it carefully over both lenses, as shown here. If cell is not straight, it will cause lenses to jam.

After casing of lens-cell is over lenses, slide fingers beneath cylinder and lift tissue, pressing lenses up into cell part way. Turn tube over slowly.

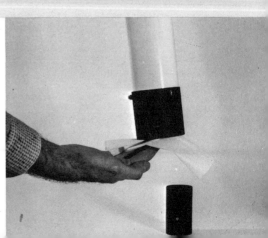

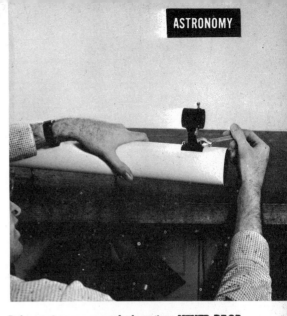

Now that objective lenses have been settled into place gingerly, the lock-ring of casing is screwed in place. No tools are used: finger-tightness only.

Before going on, a word of caution: NEVER DROP lenses into the casing. Follow photo instructions here. Next, fasten finder-mounting on scope-tube.

Rack-and-pinion eyepiece mounting comes next: it is inserted in rear end of tube, anchored in place by machine-screws through already drilled holes.

Eyepiece of small finder-scope is unscrewed so that finder-tube may be inserted through its mounting bracket, fastened to the aluminum telescope-tube.

Finder-tube is anchored in place by half-tightening wing-screws of bracket. Eyepiece is screwed back into its former position, as shown in the photograph.

Final adjustment of wing-screws to center finder-scope tightly, completes the job. All that's left: select main-scope eyepiece and search the heavens.

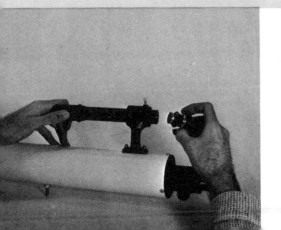

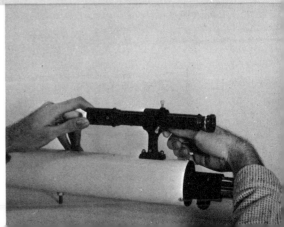

Planning Your Attic

Don't let that valuable space upstairs go to waste; there's usually plenty of room for a study, an extra bathroom or spare bedroom. It's especially suitable for the younger set.

Above, limited space problem is solved by clever arrangement of bed sliding under eaves when not in use. Right, beautiful attic room is small, yet looks larger due to well-planned gable dormer.

FEEL crowded? Children cramped into a single bedroom? No place to put things? Closets overflowing?

There's good useful space above, right in the attic to help you out. You can give each child a separate bedroom, build in enormous wardrobe closets, have a safe and spacious kiddie playroom or nursery, fix up special work areas for sewing, ham radio or other hobbies, even have your own upstairs study or studio.

When finished with wall paneling, floor planks and ceiling tiles, partitioned into rooms and outfitted with windows, dormers, fans, etc., the attic becomes part of the cubic-foot living area of the home and thus increase its value proportionately.

But first, there's the practical question of suitability of your type of attic for remodeling. Each attic presents a different situation depending on its size, pitch of the roof, accessibility and headroom.

Minimum headroom of seven feet is essential in at least part of the attic; don't forget that an enclosed ceiling must be below the roof peak so that a ventilating space will be left above it.

Space that can be used for room purposes extends outward from the center with highest clearance to points along the walls that have four-foot height from floor to rafters. These four feet are usable for beds and benches.

Some roofs are so narrow and steeply pitched that there's hardly more than a narrow catwalk in the attic with enough headroom so you can stand there. At first view, it would seem hardly possible to squeeze in a practical, decent-sized room —but don't give up hope. There's a way

Before and after photos show typical unfinished attic transformed into charming paneled bedroom.

Attic bathroom gains warmth through use of pine paneling for walls. Custom cabinet is also pine.

In this room the area under the eaves was put to good use. Long desk has lots of counter space.

Functional built-in bed under eaves has drawers to hold bed clothes, uses foam rubber mattress.

Center space of unusually large attic makes for handsome entertainment area. Note floor tiles.

to expand your attic more than double its size, with a high and level ceiling that makes possible perfect extra rooms for your family. The solution: a wide shed dormer extending along· one side of roof.

What's more, it is a project that you can do entirely yourself down to the final flashings, shingling and window framing. You won't be "raising the roof" when you do it either; take as long as you need for the job without getting the jitters that a rainstorm will wash out your home.

The present roof remains almost intact until the new dormer is enclosed; a few small openings necessary for anchoring the framework can be temporarily protected with roofing paper. The new roof, even if it has only a slight pitch, will be as solid and weather-worthy as the original one if properly flashed and shingled.

Get the assistance of an architect in planning the project; be sure to secure all required permits from your local building department to avoid complications later. Alteration of the roof line very rarely affects the stresses of the house frame.

The wide shed dormer is especially beneficial in Cape Cod, bungalow and ranch homes that have high-peaked roofs spreading all the way across to the house sides. Remember that for a minimum 7-foot 6-inch ceiling, a ridge height of at least

9 feet 6 inches above the floor (inside measurement) is necessary as the dormer ceiling joists must be below the rafters to leave a ventilating space.

Make a careful survey to decide which side of the roof to raise, how wide and high the dormer will be, how many windows it needs, what effect it will have on the appearance of the house. Consider special factors like location of stairway, plumbing and heating connection in relation to the arrangement of rooms when the area is opened up. The chimney can be included in the new roof line, if necessary.

The project involves framing out the dormer; putting in windows; sheathing the sides; covering the roof; flashing all roof and wall joints; shingling the sides and covering the roof.

Actual work starts by erecting the 2x4 front studs, tied to the house plate and joined across the top with 2x4s. Chop a hole through the eave boards at each end of the dormer width. At the same location, open holes in the roof line, level with the height of the dormer. Nail a 1x3 furring strip to the rafter at each end. Now you can put up the end studs, toe-nailed to the house plate and supported temporarily with the furring.

Put in just a few additional studs, joined to the end studs with 2x4 plates across the

Even extremely low space under eaves can be utilized for a bed or cot, especially for children.

Attic beds can easily be built by yourself out of rough scrap lumber. Foam rubber acts as mattress.

Three built-in bunks with individual night tables are lined up along this attic wall, above.

top (but no stud in a location where there will be a window). All work must be plumb and level.

Reinforce the frame with temporary bracing, if necessary. Except for the end studs, the others should not be in direct line with the present rafters. The top plate is doubled with additional 2x4s, staggering the joints. Gable plates are fitted to the corners of the frame and spiked to the present end rafters.

The next step is to remove the top boards at the ridge line for nailing on rafters, so the roof can be quickly finished and covered.

Framing is then completed with all necessary vertical studs, the sides sheathed in, roof boards nailed and window sash installed. Then strip out the old roof.

The original rafters may be taken out only after the ridge is strongly supported with at least two 4x4 posts which remain in place until the ceiling joists are spiked in. These should reach all the way across the

Shed dormer built out from roof line extends room area in finished attic. Use 2x4 framing lumber.

Windows for dormer are trimmed with regular sill and moldings, available as complete kit package.

attic and should be nailed to the rafters on the opposite side. The old rafters may then be sawed and used where needed.

Whenever your finish work for the day, cover all roof openings with tar paper secured with wood battens so that you won't have to make a hurried climb to the roof when rain threatens.

If you find that the headroom area of the attic extends to a considerable width, but is along the side that has no window openings, light may be obtained by installing small window hip dormers or gables—a much less expensive undertaking than raising the entire roof.

If the room area still seems small, remember that certain furniture such as dressers and closets are recessed into the clear space behind the wall, rather than extending into the room, thus leaving more floor space clear. Dressers are framed right into the studs so that the drawers are at the back under the eaves and the front is flush with the finished wall.

If stairs open into the only space with suitable headroom, leaving very little standing room, and you have reasons not to raise the roof level to expand the area, a practical room may still be worked into the space. Smaller sections of the attic with headroom of just over six feet can be utilized for the bathroom or sewing room.

When the layout has been planned for maximum benefit, put down a sub floor over the joists so you can walk around without fear of stumbling through the plaster ceiling below. Use rough tongue-and-groove flooring boards of lowest cost, as they will be smoothly surfaced with hardboard underlayment before the final linoleum or tiles are laid.

Now you can lay out the work directly with chalk marks, following a plan previously sketched on paper. Use chalk to mark off the framing lines so they can be studied before actual work begins.

If it is necessary to put in a new stairway, study the alternative locations. If

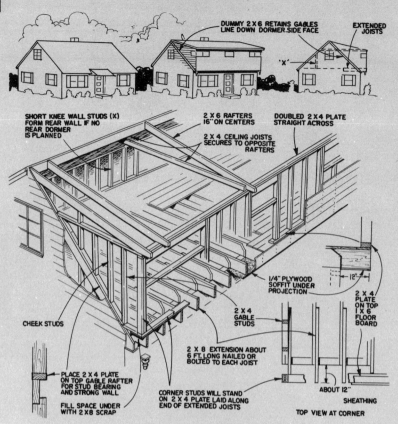

DUMMY 2 X 6 RETAINS GABLES LINE DOWN DORMER.SIDE FACE

EXTENDED JOISTS

'X'

SHORT KNEE WALL STUDS (X) FORM REAR WALL IF NO REAR DORMER IS PLANNED

2 X 6 RAFTERS 16" ON CENTERS

2 X 4 CEILING JOISTS SECURES TO OPPOSITE RAFTERS

DOUBLED 2 X 4 PLATE STRAIGHT ACROSS

1/4" PLYWOOD SOFFIT UNDER PROJECTION

2 X 4 PLATE ON TOP 1 X 6 FLOOR BOARD

CHEEK STUDS

2 X 4 GABLE STUDS

PLACE 2 X 4 PLATE ON TOP GABLE RAFTER FOR STUD BEARING AND STRONG WALL

FILL SPACE UNDER WITH 2 X 8 SCRAP

2 X 8 EXTENSION ABOUT 6 FT. LONG NAILED OR BOLTED TO EACH JOIST

CORNER STUDS WILL STAND ON 2 X 4 PLATE LAID ALONG END OF EXTENDED JOISTS

ABOUT 12"

SHEATHING

TOP VIEW AT CORNER

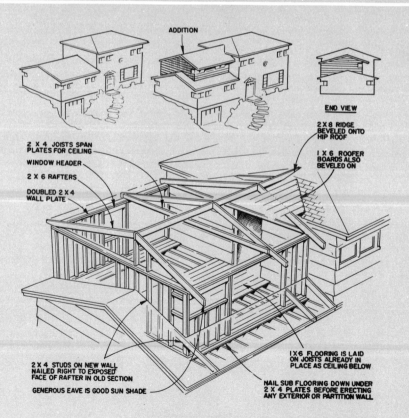

ADDITION

END VIEW

2 X 4 JOISTS SPAN PLATES FOR CEILING

WINDOW HEADER

2 X 6 RAFTERS

DOUBLED 2 X 4 WALL PLATE

2 X 8 RIDGE BEVELED ONTO HIP ROOF

1 X 6 ROOFER BOARDS ALSO BEVELED ON

2 X 4 STUDS ON NEW WALL NAILED RIGHT TO EXPOSED FACE OF RAFTER IN OLD SECTION

GENEROUS EAVE IS GOOD SUN SHADE

1 X 6 FLOORING IS LAID ON JOISTS ALREADY IN PLACE AS CEILING BELOW

NAIL SUB FLOORING DOWN UNDER 2 X 4 PLATES BEFORE ERECTING ANY EXTERIOR OR PARTITION WALL

152

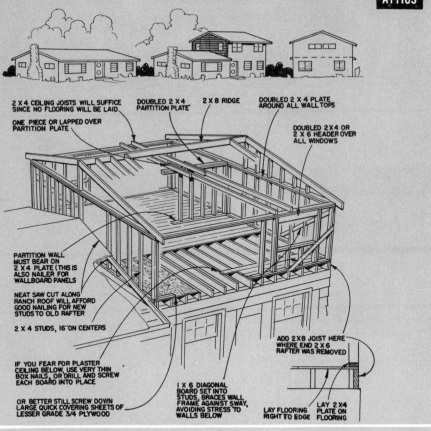

2 X 4 CEILING JOISTS WILL SUFFICE
SINCE NO FLOORING WILL BE LAID

DOUBLED 2 X 4
PARTITION PLATE

2 X 8 RIDGE

DOUBLED 2 X 4 PLATE
AROUND ALL WALL TOPS

ONE PIECE OR LAPPED OVER
PARTITION PLATE

DOUBLED 2 X 4 OR
2 X 6 HEADER OVER
ALL WINDOWS

PARTITION WALL
MUST BEAR ON
2 X 4 PLATE (THIS IS
ALSO NAILER FOR
WALLBOARD PANELS

NEAT SAW CUT ALONG
RANCH ROOF WILL AFFORD
GOOD NAILING FOR NEW
STUDS TO OLD RAFTER

2 X 4 STUDS, 16" ON CENTERS

ADD 2 X 8 JOIST HERE
WHERE END 2 X 6
RAFTER WAS REMOVED

IF YOU FEAR FOR PLASTER
CEILING BELOW, USE VERY THIN
BOX NAILS, OR DRILL AND SCREW
EACH BOARD INTO PLACE

1 X 6 DIAGONAL
BOARD SET INTO
STUDS, BRACES WALL
FRAME AGAINST SWAY,
AVOIDING STRESS TO
WALLS BELOW

OR BETTER STILL SCREW DOWN
LARGE QUICK COVERING SHEETS OF
LESSER GRADE 3/4 PLYWOOD

LAY FLOORING
RIGHT TO EDGE

LAY 2 X 4
PLATE ON
FLOORING

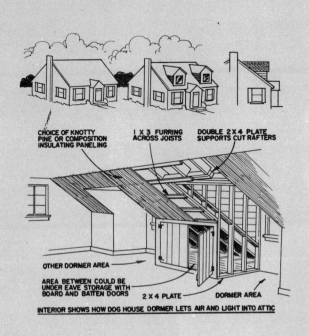

CHOICE OF KNOTTY
PINE OR COMPOSITION
INSULATING PANELING

1 X 3 FURRING
ACROSS JOISTS

DOUBLE 2 X 4 PLATE
SUPPORTS CUT RAFTERS

OTHER DORMER AREA

AREA BETWEEN COULD BE
UNDER EAVE STORAGE WITH
BOARD AND BATTEN DOORS

2 X 4 PLATE

DORMER AREA

INTERIOR SHOWS HOW DOG HOUSE DORMER LETS AIR AND LIGHT INTO ATTIC

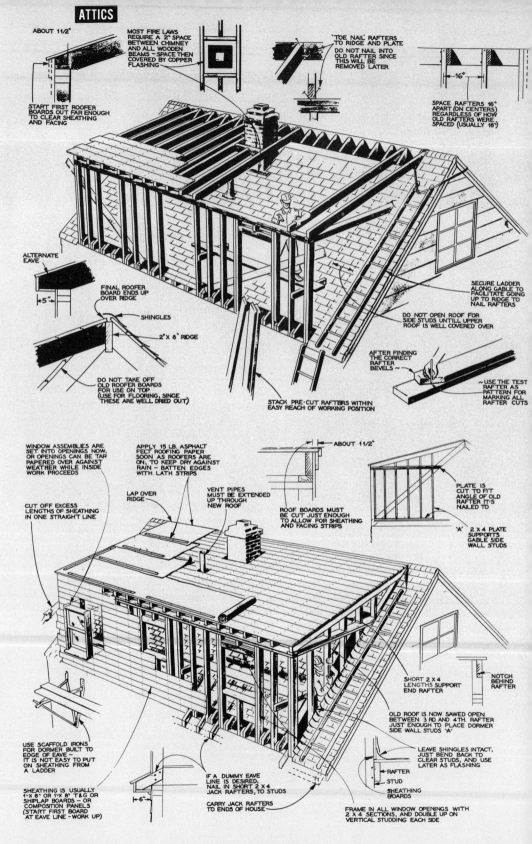

ABOUT 11/2"

START FIRST ROOFER BOARDS OUT FAR ENOUGH TO CLEAR SHEATHING AND FACING

MOST FIRE LAWS REQUIRE A 2" SPACE BETWEEN CHIMNEY AND ALL WOODEN BEAMS — SPACE THEN COVERED BY COPPER FLASHING

'TOE NAIL' RAFTERS TO RIDGE AND PLATE

DO NOT NAIL INTO OLD RAFTER SINCE THIS WILL BE REMOVED LATER

16"

SPACE RAFTERS 16" APART (ON CENTERS) REGARDLESS OF HOW OLD RAFTERS WERE SPACED (USUALLY 18")

ALTERNATE EAVE

5"

FINAL ROOFER BOARD ENDS UP OVER RIDGE

SHINGLES

2"X 8" RIDGE

DO NOT TAKE OFF OLD ROOFER BOARDS FOR USE ON TOP (USE FOR FLOORING, SINCE THESE ARE WELL DRIED OUT)

SECURE LADDER ALONG GABLE TO FACILITATE GOING UP TO RIDGE TO NAIL RAFTERS

DO NOT OPEN ROOF FOR SIDE STUDS UNTILL UPPER ROOF IS WELL COVERED OVER

AFTER FINDING THE CORRECT RAFTER BEVELS ~

~ USE THE TEST RAFTER AS PATTERN FOR MARKING ALL RAFTER CUTS

STACK PRE-CUT RAFTERS WITHIN EASY REACH OF WORKING POSITION

WINDOW ASSEMBLIES ARE SET INTO OPENINGS NOW, OR OPENINGS CAN BE TAR PAPERED OVER AGAINST WEATHER WHILE INSIDE WORK PROCEEDS

APPLY 15 LB. ASPHALT FELT ROOFING PAPER SOON AS ROOFERS ARE ON, TO KEEP DRY AGAINST RAIN — BATTEN EDGES WITH LATH STRIPS

ABOUT 11/2"

CUT OFF EXCESS LENGTHS OF SHEATHING IN ONE STRAIGHT LINE

LAP OVER RIDGE

VENT PIPES MUST BE EXTENDED UP THROUGH NEW ROOF

ROOF BOARDS MUST BE CUT JUST ENOUGH TO ALLOW FOR SHEATHING AND FACING STRIPS

PLATE IS CUT TO FIT ANGLE OF OLD RAFTER IT'S NAILED TO

'A' 2 X 4 PLATE SUPPORTS GABLE SIDE WALL STUDS

SHORT 2 X 4 LENGTHS SUPPORT END RAFTER

NOTCH BEHIND RAFTER

USE SCAFFOLD IRONS FOR DORMER BUILT TO EDGE OF EAVE — IT IS NOT EASY TO PUT ON SHEATHING FROM A LADDER

OLD ROOF IS NOW SAWED OPEN BETWEEN 3 RD. AND 4TH. RAFTER JUST ENOUGH TO PLACE DORMER SIDE WALL STUDS 'A'

LEAVE SHINGLES INTACT, JUST BEND BACK TO CLEAR STUDS, AND USE LATER AS FLASHING

RAFTER

STUD

SHEATHING BOARDS

SHEATHING IS USUALLY 1"X 6" OR 1"X 8" T&G OR SHIPLAP BOARDS — OR COMPOSITION PANELS (START FIRST BOARD AT EAVE LINE - WORK UP)

6"

IF A DUMMY EAVE LINE IS DESIRED, NAIL IN SHORT 2 X 4 JACK RAFTERS, TO STUDS

CARRY JACK RAFTERS TO ENDS OF HOUSE

FRAME IN ALL WINDOW OPENINGS WITH 2 X 4 SECTIONS, AND DOUBLE UP ON VERTICAL STUDDING EACH SIDE

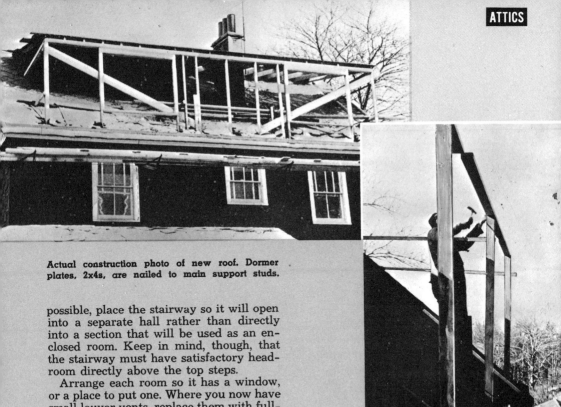

Actual construction photo of new roof. Dormer plates, 2x4s, are nailed to main support studs.

possible, place the stairway so it will open into a separate hall rather than directly into a section that will be used as an enclosed room. Keep in mind, though, that the stairway must have satisfactory headroom directly above the top steps.

Arrange each room so it has a window, or a place to put one. Where you now have small louver vents, replace them with full-size windows when you frame out the walls. The louver vents will be installed instead in the area above the ceiling. •

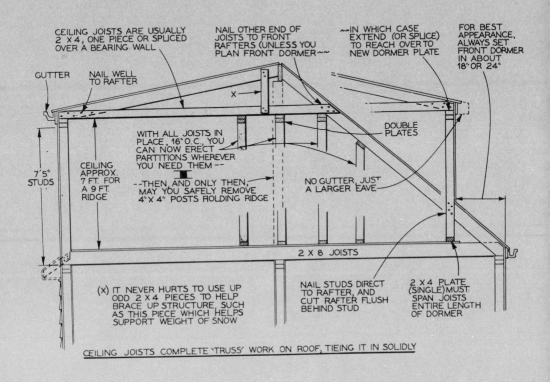

CEILING JOISTS ARE USUALLY 2 X 4, ONE PIECE OR SPLICED OVER A BEARING WALL

NAIL OTHER END OF JOISTS TO FRONT RAFTERS (UNLESS YOU PLAN FRONT DORMER~~

~~IN WHICH CASE EXTEND (OR SPLICE) TO REACH OVER TO NEW DORMER PLATE

FOR BEST APPEARANCE, ALWAYS SET FRONT DORMER IN ABOUT 18˝ OR 24˝

GUTTER

NAIL WELL TO RAFTER

X

WITH ALL JOISTS IN PLACE, 16˝ O.C., YOU CAN NOW ERECT PARTITIONS WHEREVER YOU NEED THEM --

DOUBLE PLATES

7´5˝ STUDS

CEILING APPROX. 7 FT. FOR A 9 FT. RIDGE

--THEN, AND ONLY THEN, MAY YOU SAFELY REMOVE 4˝ X 4˝ POSTS HOLDING RIDGE

NO GUTTER, JUST A LARGER EAVE

2 X 8 JOISTS

(X) IT NEVER HURTS TO USE UP ODD 2 X 4 PIECES TO HELP BRACE UP STRUCTURE, SUCH AS THIS PIECE WHICH HELPS SUPPORT WEIGHT OF SNOW

NAIL STUDS DIRECT TO RAFTER, AND CUT RAFTER FLUSH BEHIND STUD

2 X 4 PLATE (SINGLE) MUST SPAN JOISTS ENTIRE LENGTH OF DORMER

CEILING JOISTS COMPLETE 'TRUSS' WORK ON ROOF, TIEING IT IN SOLIDLY

Attic Access

New types of disappearing staircases sold in
kit form are easy to install, enable you to
utilize previously inaccessible living space.

IN the "good old days" homes were built with real stairways leading to a spacious attic which was divided into a number of small rooms. But most houses built in the last 25 years, except for high-roofed bungalow style homes, have only a small hatchway located inside a closet or other inconvenient location, with just a tiny wall ladder to reach into the attic.

Many a homeowner boasts that, he "hasn't been up to the attic in 10 years," and evidently he's referring to the worthiness of his roof. Any trouble during that time might have forced him to squeeze through the closet hatchway to inspect the attic.

But there's good space up there that can be an important part of the family living area. If your home is one without an attic stairway there is, fortunately, a ready-made solution. Several types of prefabricated stairways and disappearing ladders are available, and one of them surely will serve your purpose even if there is only a minimum overhead clearance at the access position. These stairways are sturdy, moderate in cost and easy to install.

In some cases, where there is an open section of suitable size at one end of a hall, a conventional full-size staircase may be installed by cutting an opening into the ceiling. The staircase is purchased custom built according to specifications so it will fit the dimensions and location. The stairs come partly assembled with stringers and treads fitted and nailed together. Installation requires only bolting or nailing against the ceiling joists and locking the lower ends to the floor. Newel posts, handrail and banisters are added to complete the installation. If the fittings are carefully selected your new stairway will

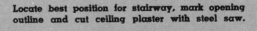

Very little effort is required to pull folded stair sections down with help of stick, as shown.

Locate best position for stairway, mark opening outline and cut ceiling plaster with steel saw.

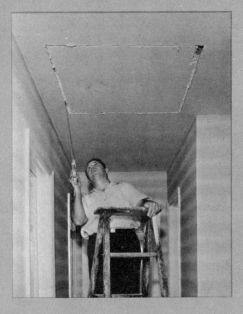

Plaster is pulled off in several large sections. Cover floor below to catch all dust.

make a handsome addition to the house and your attic will be open for convenient everyday use.

Disappearing staircases come packed as a complete box unit. One type is in three hinged sections which fold compactly on a plywood panel mounted into a ceiling opening. This stairway is operated by pulling down the panel from the ceiling with a short dowel stick, which brings the lower sections of the stairway within reach so they can be unfolded to extend to the floor. There is a handrail along most of the stair length. Hinge and coil spring balance mechanism are completely concealed when the door is closed.

A full-length staircase which disappears straight up into the attic requires at least 4 feet 6 inches headroom above the attic floor. Installation requires an opening 26 inches wide, 54 inches long.

Another type of door has just two stair sections. Assembly is contained on a single plywood panel with counterbalancing springs. Stairs are extended automatically with the same chain that pulls down the panel. The lower half of the stairs moves forward when the ceiling panel comes into open position. This type of stairway requires a ceiling opening ranging from 24x54 inches to 30x60 inches, depending on the size and stair model. As a general rule, it will pay you to get the largest stairway that can be fitted into the available hall space.

Study the location and the attic floor above to check the clearance to the rafters if they are close by. Try to work out the position so there will be minimum sawing of the floor joists, though installation need not weaken the strength of the floor, regardless of whether they run parallel or perpendicular to the opening that must be made.

In actual installation, first outline the required opening on the ceiling, drill holes

joists are cut next. Make saw cut two inches from edge of opening to allow for the 2x6 header.

The cut-off joists may be used as headers, are nailed into joist ends to reinforce attic floor.

Staircase frame is nailed right to the joists. Note spring-hinge arrangement for easy folding.

All that shows of stairs is a plywood panel which is framed with a molding to hide the cut plaster.

in the corners, then saw the plaster along the lines. The ceiling opening is the full size of the stair frame. Sawing of the plaster may be done with a portable electric saw, using a special hardened blade, or a pointed keyhole-type saw, also with a special metal cutting blade. The teeth of a regular wood cutting blade will be worn down quickly if you use it to cut plaster. Where the saw hits the joists so you can't maneuver it, cut the plaster at that point with a chisel.

When the cutting is all done, break the plaster free in large pieces. This will open the area under the joists and make sawing easier. Spread a drop cloth or paper on the floor to catch the plaster dust. In sawing the joists remember that you must allow enough space for putting in double headers at each end. The headers are lapped at half thickness for joining solidly to the joists. Mark off the positions and saw through only half the width of the

joists. Where possible, continue the headers across to the far joists at each side, cutting notches to hold the headers solid.

The space between the joists will be larger than the ceiling opening, and you now close it in with the cut away beam which is nailed to the end headers. The rough opening should then be the correct size specified.

The stairway now is opened with the frame set in place, supported across one end with a board spanning the opening. Put in a couple of nails temporarily at the end that is flush with the floor, then pull the support from underneath and nail the other end after checking with a spirit level.

Try the stairway to see if it works easily. If necessary, drive wedges along the sides to shim the frame in the opening. The frame must be level for the stairway and balance springs to operate. Ceiling plaster edges are finished off with trim molding. •

Walls

and

Insulation

IN most homes, studs of the outside wall frame may be used also for the finished inside walls. All that is needed is to pack insulation batts between the studs and cover with wall paneling. If knotty pine paneling will be used, put furring over the studs. Taller wall areas are best suited for placement of windows. Studs, therefore, must be sawed here above and below the window. These cutaway studs must be reinforced with double headers across top and bottom supported with 2x4 inserts to carry the weight.

Along the rest of the room put up side-wall studs resting on 2x4 floor plates nailed to the sides of the rafters or, for a better

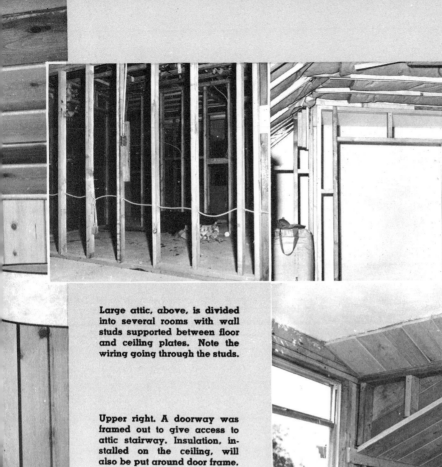

Large attic, above, is divided into several rooms with wall studs supported between floor and ceiling plates. Note the wiring going through the studs.

Upper right. A doorway was framed out to give access to attic stairway. Insulation, installed on the ceiling, will also be put around door frame.

Insulating batts, right, are fitted between the uprights in this attic wall. The vapor barrier side of the batt must always face to inside of room.

job, angle-cut these shorter studs so that they fit against the slope of the rafters and are toenailed in from the sides. These hip walls should be at least four feet high to end the room before the ceiling slopes away to the floor.

Thorough insulation is important to keep your new attic rooms comfortable in summer's heat and winter's cold. Very likely the floor joists already were packed with insulating batts, but now the walls and new ceiling must be protected. This is a job you might well do yourself, however, only complete coverage, which means that no single spot is left uncovered, will give effective heat control.

Use insulating batts two or three inches thick to fit between the 16-inch studs and joists. The batts have a heavy wrapping with flanges on each side that open up flat and are used for stapling in place. When short lengths are used, the ends are overlapped or butted tightly.

One thing to keep in mind is that the vapor barrier, or foil side, of the batt faces inside the room. This tends to prevent moisture-laden air from penetrating into the insulation wool where it will be trapped and may cause rotting of the beams.

Most of the job goes very quickly—in fact, it will take but a few hours to pack in batts right along the walls and ceiling.

Aluminum foil acts as vapor barrier and can be stapled over insulating batts to prevent moisture.

Tongue-and-groove pine paneling is installed over the insulation.

At the time of wall installation, attic windows, doors and dormers are also framed and paneled.

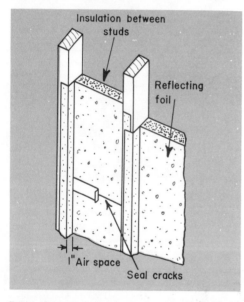

Insulation between studs

Reflecting foil

1" Air space

Seal cracks

Compact spare room in attic is attractively faced with wall panels, has home-built bed and chests.

Hardwood panels may be fitted over special clips attached to furring. Note how foil is facing room.

Wallboard in attic is inexpensive, gives smooth surface. Boards are nailed over the insulation along wall and continued up along sloped ceiling; rest of ceiling may then be finished with acoustical tiles.

Then comes the most difficult part of filling in odd corners, such as around windows, over door frames, at open corners, etc. It's not necessary to insulate beyond the walls, that is, along the eaves and other unfinished parts of the attic area. Just make sure that all rooms that will be used are well protected.

Before putting up partition framing, nail collar beams across the rafters at suitable height, so there's no interference with lifting the long beams to the rafters. These are either 2x4s or 2x6s, angle-sawed to clear the roof boards and nailed into the rafters through the sides.

The partition studs are 2x4s on sill plates, nailed to the rafters or the collar beams. At corners of the partition and at all door openings use double studs. Where studs are not in the positions of the rafters, put in bridging to provide a nailing support. It's a good idea, too, to install horizontal bridging between studs to stiffen the frame.

You will find it easier to pre-build the partition frame in one piece right on the floor and raise it for nailing to top and side supports. This method eliminates slow toenailing and also is more sturdy because the top and bottom plates are nailed in through the ends. It also solves problems where framing supports are lacking. Lay out the studs needed for the entire wall, nail on the plates along top and bottom, then tip the frame into upright position so the sill plates can be nailed in to hold the frame solidly. Watch that the plate at

doorway openings is not nailed in, as it will have to be cut away at those places.

Frame stud spacing of 16 inches is preferable, though 24-inch centers are also acceptable. The closer spacing makes insulation easier and offers a better base for nailing Sheetrock and wallboard. If you plan to use knotty pine paneling, apply rows of horizontal furring across the studs for nailing the boards. Corners require additional furring for nailing panels that turn to the side wall, though strips of 1x2-inch furring nailed to the edge of the stud will also serve as a nailing surface.

It's a good idea to put wallboard or Sheetrock at least over outside wall framing, even if the wall finish will be of another material. Over the ceiling beams wallboard, too, provides additional insulating surface to seal any opening. Furring for ceiling panels or tiles are nailed 12 inches apart across the beams.

After framing the entire room, "rough in" all electrical and plumbing connections before proceeding with wall finish and other details.

Before putting up any wall panels, however, consider the installation of built-in furniture, which can go behind the studs and fit into the eaves, thus saving a great amount of valuable space. Dressers, bookcases, closets, etc., can be installed flush with the room walls, yet have plenty of space behind, extending into the eaves area. Make your plans now, before you expend a lot of needless labor. •

Attic Floor and Ceiling

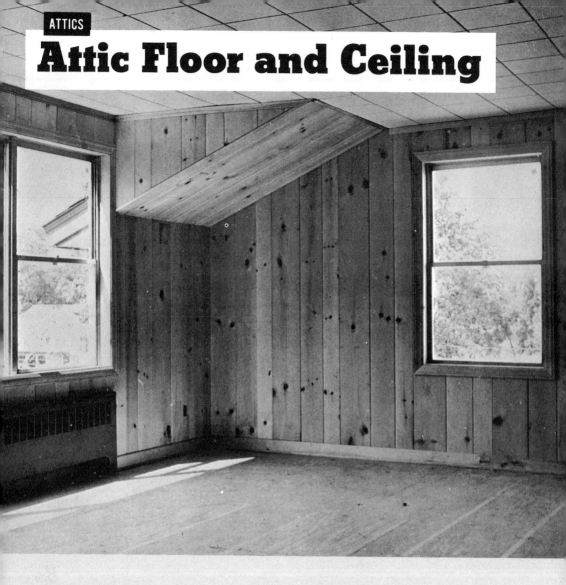

ONE of the first steps in making the attic usable is finishing the floor. In some homes the attic may have a rough flooring, but in many others there are just uncovered joists with perhaps a narrow strip of flooring across the attic. This condition should not be permitted to remain while you proceed with other work because there's always the possibility of slipping off the end of a joist and finding your foot projecting through the ceiling plaster of a bedroom below.

The only preliminary work, prior to finishing the floor, would be to bring up any required wiring, often by splicing to existing fixtures on the ceiling below. Usually, it is better to have a completely new circuit going straight into the attic to eliminate

additional drain on the house current. Now all is ready.

Floor finishing should start with laying a rough underfloor of lowest-cost, tongue-and-groove boards, face nailed right to the joists and extending over the entire attic area, even covering sections that will not be finished into rooms; the spaces under eaves behind room walls may well be used for storage purposes. In any event, it's just as easy to cover the entire area as it would be to fit boards into special sections.

The rough flooring should be finished off with a good surface. This may be oak boards or blocks, but if you intend to put down floor tiles or carpeting, it would be just as well to finish the floor inexpensively with Masonite underlayment, nailed down carefully with special screw-type nails which are spaced four inches apart on all directions. The idea is to get that underlayment down so tightly that there's no chance for squeaking and popping of the nails later. This composition board underlayment also has a sound-insulating value that you'll be thankful for later, when the formerly completely quiet attic becomes a center of activity.

For this reason, too, you should select the finish floor tiles or linoleum for resilience and quietness. Rugs and carpets are good in most cases, but for a nursery or teen bedroom you may prefer a smooth tile floor.

Cork tiles are particularly good from this standpoint; rubber tiles also have excellent resiliency and sound-deadening qualities in addition to color, are easy to keep in their attractive brightness. The floor coverings may vary for each room according to the special need, and the hardboard underlayment will be suitable for each condition.

However, before putting in your finish floor, complete all electric work and other tasks. The finish flooring is tackled only when most of the other work is out of the way, so that there won't be scratches from carpentry work and handling of materials.

Partitioning the rooms follows the standard procedure for stud framing and door

enclosures, as described before, except that the support plates are nailed directly to the floor and ceiling joists.

The new 24-inch width of Armstrong's linoleum makes installation easy. A layer of hardboard over the subfloor will give you the smooth, level surface essential for a good finish floor regardless of whether it is linoleum tiles or other material. Use ¼-inch hardboard in 4x4-foot sheets, laid rough side up with a clearance of about $\frac{1}{32}$ inch, the thickness of a knife blade, between the panel edges for expansion. Arrange the panels so the ends are staggered.

The hardboard is nailed down with ringed or "screw-type" nails, spaced four inches apart in each direction, to give every part of the panel a tight fit with no chance for bubbling up or developing squeaks. This will take quite a lot of nailing, but it's worth the resulting trouble-free floor and longer lasting linoleum. Just spill out a package of nails on the floor and start hammering—a few hours will do the job and you will know that it is done well.

Next comes a layer of felt paper, put down with regular linoleum paste, spread with a special notched trowel supplied with the installation kit sold by all linoleum dealers.

Cut the felt paper with shears accurately to size running the narrower length of the room, spread just enough adhesive for the

Ceiling should be well insulated above the furring strips. Carefully check with level to avoid unsightly bulges later on. If necessary, shim out furring strips with scrap pieces of plywood to obtain even surface.

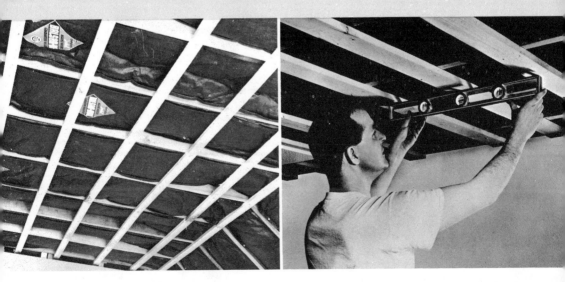

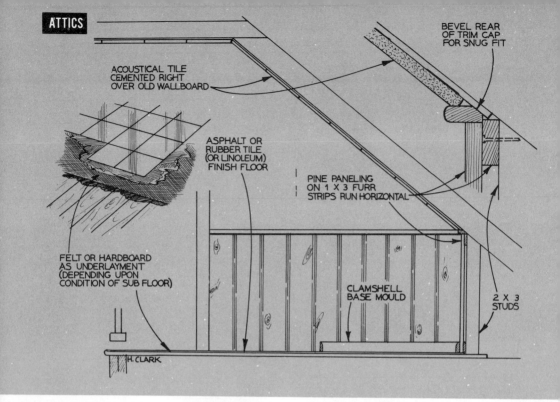

ACOUSTICAL TILE
CEMENTED RIGHT
OVER OLD WALLBOARD

BEVEL REAR
OF TRIM CAP
FOR SNUG FIT

ASPHALT OR
RUBBER TILE
(OR LINOLEUM)
FINISH FLOOR

PINE PANELING
ON 1 X 3 FURR
STRIPS RUN HORIZONTAL

FELT OR HARDBOARD
AS UNDERLAYMENT
(DEPENDING UPON
CONDITION OF SUB FLOOR)

CLAMSHELL
BASE MOULD

2 X 3
STUDS

H. CLARK

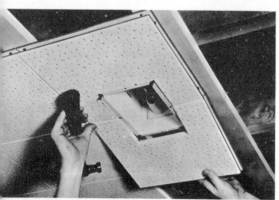

Cut tiles for recessed light fixtures. Glass cover goes over tiles, is held with thumb screws.

Use a fiberboard knife to cut around hanging fixtures. Trace pattern carefully to avoid waste.

Tongue-and-groove acoustical tiles are available for easy installation. Nail or staple to furring.

Tiles may be painted to match or contrast room decor; the factory coating on tile acts as primer.

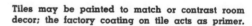

strip and lay out the felt paper. It should be rolled out to assure good bond to the underfloor—a lawn roller will do fine, but you also can do it with a small hand roller.

Linoleum is laid in half the room at a time, with the 24-inch-wide linoleum strips running parallel to the longer walls to keep the number of seams to a minimum. Also, because the felt paper was laid across the shorter sides of the room, this will keep the linoleum across the felt seams rather than over them.

Each strip of linoleum is cut to size for where it is to go, before the adhesive is troweled on the floor. A good system is to fit all the strips needed for the room before any of them are pasted down.

While you can just place the first strip against the wall base, depending on cove molding to cover any open spaces between the linoleum and the wall, a more efficient and professional installation is to "scribe in" and cut the linoleum to fit snug along the entire wall, so that all irregularities in the wall line are filled in.

Marking is done with a special 18-inch scriber tool sold by Armstrong dealers, or a pair of regular dividers with sharp pointed ends. The linoleum to be fitted is cut to oversize length, the ends curled up out of the way and the strip pushed up against the baseboard, or as closely as it will go while remaining at a true straight line to the wall. Keep the dividers in vertical position and draw along the entire length of the wall, allowing the point to score the surface of the linoleum. Thus, the contour of the baseboard has been transferred to the plastic.

Use a hooked-blade linoleum knife for cutting. The blade must be kept sharp by honing it occasionally so it cuts without much pressure. A little practice will enable you to do this cutting easily and accurately.

The strip of linoleum is pushed back so the edge is along the wall, and the ends cut in to fit. Do this by flashing up the ends of the linoleum against the wall, then forcing the material down into the floor corner. When you get the correct outline, cut through slowly, bit by bit, to get a close fit. Continue with the next strips until all the floor is covered, marking numbers on the back of each strip in rotation. Where necessary, each strip should be cut to fit around any projection in the wall, and along door casings, thresholds, radiators, etc.

When all is ready, return to the first strip and spread adhesive for one section at a time. It's better to roll each strip right after it is laid, before the adhesive can

PARTITIONS RUNNING WITH JOISTS MUST PROVIDE CORNER, OR EDGE, FOR NAILING CEILING TILE — FOUR EXAMPLES SHOWN

1 X 2 EDGE NAILERS BUTT TO PLATE

1 X 6 CROSS BRACE

WALL PLATE

WALLS ARE NAILED HERE

STUD

1 X 6 OR 1 X 8 ON TOP OF PLATE

1 X 6 BRACE

PLATE

TOE NAIL FURRING TO 1X 6

TILE

STUD

1 X 2 OR 1 X 3 FURRING

1 X 6 OR 8 UNDER JOIST WITH 2 X 4 PLATE UNDER

1 X 2 OR 3 FURRING NAILED UNDER JOISTS FIRST

PLATE NAILED UNDER FURRING

harden. Clean up any paste on the surface with a damp cloth as you go.

Installation of resilient tiles such as vinyl, cork, asphalt, linoleum or rubber follows the same procedure as explained earlier

The only difference in the attic will be the laying of felt paper as underlayment on the wood floor.

Attic Ceiling

Ceiling finishing in the attic differs somewhat from that of the basement, described earlier, because the ceiling often is irregular, with some sections sloped gradually while others may drift off into sharply angled corners. Also, the attic rooms will be used primarily as bedrooms and you may want them to resemble other rooms of the house, with conventional ceil-

ing surfaces rather than a fancy finish.

Thus, the ceiling may be of gypsum board which is curved gradually to hide the sharp wall angles for a more subtle slope. With these large panels you can make the ceiling merge into the upper part of a wall for a feeling of continuity, and to permit a single type of decoration over the wall and ceiling.

For maximum comfort you couldn't do better than to finish the room ceilings with really effective acoustical tiles such as Armstrong's Cushiontone, which subdues even the noise of children's games and teen parties. These tiles have ⅜-inch tongues for stapling. Another effective and good-looking ceiling surface is obtained with Templock tiles in white or ivory color, available in the following sizes: 12x12

To give smooth surface for linoleum or floor tiles, cover subfloor with 4'x4' hardboard panels. Use panels full size except where they will not fit.

Joints of hardboard underlayment should be staggered. Allow a slight separation between the panels, 1/32", about the thickness of a knife blade.

Linoleum can be fitted perfectly against any irregular contour by using a scriber, as shown. Cut outline with a sharp, hooked linoleum knife.

Put felt paper over the hardboard underlayment before installing the linoleum, and attach with adhesive. Use special trowel for applying paste.

inches, 16x16 inches, 16x32 inches and 12x24 inches; they are centerscored and tongue-and-grooved for easy installation, either by stapling or nailing to wood furring on the wide-flange Lok-Bevel joints; the fastening is never visible.

Once the furring is up, all the tools you'll need for putting up the ceiling tiles are a spring-type stapler, a rule, crosscut saw or fiberboard knife.

The acoustical tile may be put up directly to the furring, or over wallboard which has been nailed to the furring. But in the latter case, be sure that the furring strips are straight and uniformly spaced so that you'll reach them with the nails. Staples won't hold in the wallboard so nails must be used instead.

Start at a corner, setting the two tongue edges into the corner, facing opposite walls. The first course, or border, of tiles against the wall must be sawed to fit between the last furring strip flush with the wall and the center of the first furring away from the wall.

From there, work your way across the room, fitting the joints together and putting four staples into each tile through the tongue, even with the furring, and one staple through the opposite corner.

Wherever necessary to clear ceiling light fixtures, or to fit inside corners, cut the tile to shape with a crosscut or coping saw, or a fiberboard knife. At wall ends, drive a final 6-penny nail into the face of the tile close to the wall; these nails will be covered by the cove molding used to finish off the ceiling. •

Before laying down tiles, measure your room and, using a snap chalk line, mark off center point. This will divide the area into four equal parts.

To get around pipes or other obstructions, use a compass to draw circle equal to size of pipe. Cut a slit to center of the circle using a sharp linoleum knife.

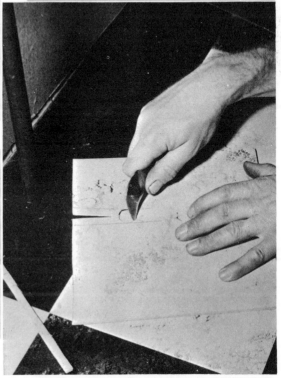

Before applying adhesive, lay tiles along center lines, as shown, to determine the best starting point. All border tiles should be the same size.

A Room in the Attic

A combined bedroom, playroom and study featuring knotty pine is built in the attic for a boy.

By Lee Fogel

A GROWING family can soon lead to congestion in a small house. Knowing that we would be faced with such a problem, we planned from the beginning to add extra living space in the unfinished attic of our story-and-a-half, two-bedroom home. This led us to have an extra dormer installed when the house was being built; and when the need arose, we were prepared with the design illustrated on these pages.

This particular house is part of a de-

View shows the recess into which the bed fits by day. Showing behind the bookcase is entrance to storage space under eave.

Half of bed, projecting from recess, is used as couch in daytime; full width is used here. Bookcase hides storage area.

Construction around the dormer window is shown above. This will be the study area.

Using level to check alignment of 2x4's which form inner wall in front of eave.

velopment—the houses around it being of similar design. Before planning of the room was carried out we canvassed the neighbors to learn what had been done along the same lines. In this way it was discovered what had turned out to be good and what "we would do differently if we had it to do again." In one instance a man had failed to provide a way to get behind the attic walls and later found it necessary to break through. This bit of information led to proper access being provided in the new design. We also had the opportunity to see how some of our own ideas had worked out and, therefore, either retained or discarded them.

The next step was to make a rough sketch on paper. It was decided that a room for our boy should be as much a self-contained unit as possible—by day, a study and playroom where there would be ample room for a group of children and plenty of storage space for toys and, by night, a bedroom. The design was worked out along these lines.

The key feature was to be a wall containing a recessed bed; a bookcase which rolls out on casters to permit use of the space near the eave for storing trunks and suitcases; a built-in chest of drawers; and a baseboard which lifts up to expose a floor-level aperture for storing a 4x6-ft. track platform (on casters) for a toy train.

The bed recess was made as long as the bed and 13 in. deep. At night, the bed would be pulled out so that its full width can be used for sleeping; by day, it was to be moved far enough into the wall to give the room more play area,

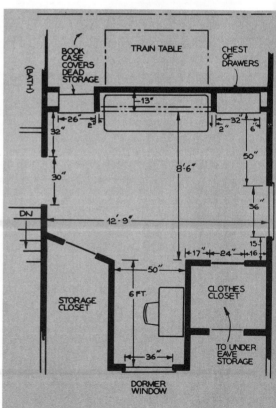

Checking the measurements of the opening into which the bookcase will be recessed.

The boy and his friends enjoy themselves. Paper above them has space ship pattern.

but not so far in that it could not be used for sitting or reclining.

Opposite this wall, it was decided to put a study nook in the dormer which had been added at the beginning. Two large closets were laid out to flank the

dormer—one for clothes and the other for storage. This arrangement left a clear rectangle (12'-9"x8'-6") in the center.

With the sub-flooring in, it was decided that the best procedure would be

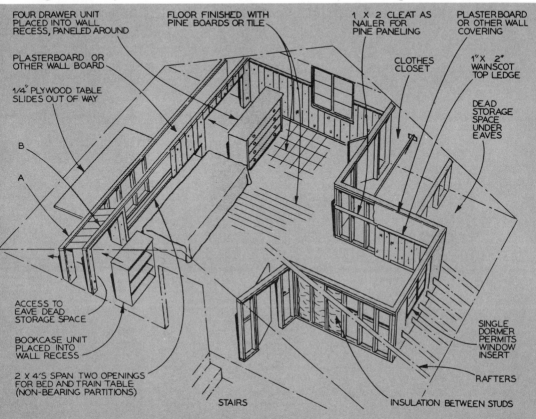

FOUR DRAWER UNIT PLACED INTO WALL RECESS, PANELED AROUND

FLOOR FINISHED WITH PINE BOARDS OR TILE

1 X 2 CLEAT AS NAILER FOR PINE PANELING

PLASTERBOARD OR OTHER WALL COVERING

PLASTERBOARD OR OTHER WALL BOARD

CLOTHES CLOSET

1" X 2" WAINSCOT TOP LEDGE

1/4" PLYWOOD TABLE SLIDES OUT OF WAY

DEAD STORAGE SPACE UNDER EAVES

B

A

ACCESS TO EAVE DEAD STORAGE SPACE

BOOKCASE UNIT PLACED INTO WALL RECESS

SINGLE DORMER PERMITS WINDOW INSERT

2 X 4'S SPAN TWO OPENINGS FOR BED AND TRAIN TABLE (NON-BEARING PARTITIONS)

RAFTERS

STAIRS

INSULATION BETWEEN STUDS

to chalk the full scale outlines of our paper sketch on the attic floor. This permitted a better visualization of the plan and gave the opportunity to make a change which, otherwise, we might not have considered. It was found that by angling one of the closet walls, we could have more storage space without detracting from the open feeling of the room.

The next step was to select the materials. For long service, easy maintenance, attractive appearance and cost, we finally picked a knotty western pine paneling for the lower walls. Specifically, the wood is random width Idaho white pine. Pine was also selected for the flooring. For the upper walls and ceiling, a paper with a pattern of space ships was chosen.

The planning completed, actual work was begun. A 2x4 plate and studs were installed for the walls, leaving space for the bed recess and train board opening. When the bed is pushed in it goes only as far as the inner wall. However, the train board passes under the inner wall.

to the eave. A horizontal 2x4 was carried across above the plate of the inner wall, high enough to allow the train board to slide under. Another 2x4 was carried across at the top of the bed opening in the outer wall. Then the interior of the recess was closed up with plasterboard. Finally, the recesses for the chest of drawers and the bookcase were framed up.

When the framing was in, the wiring was completed and the electrical outlets installed. Then the pine paneling was carried into the attic and stacked, with air spaces between, so that it could adjust to the conditions. It remained that way for more than a week. In the meantime, plasterboard was installed on the upper walls and ceiling.

The paneling, itself, was rubbed with steel wool before installation and cutouts were made in panels covering the outlet boxes. To eliminate waste, each section of the room was measured carefully and the random width panels shuffled around until a proper fit was realized for a particular section. The panels

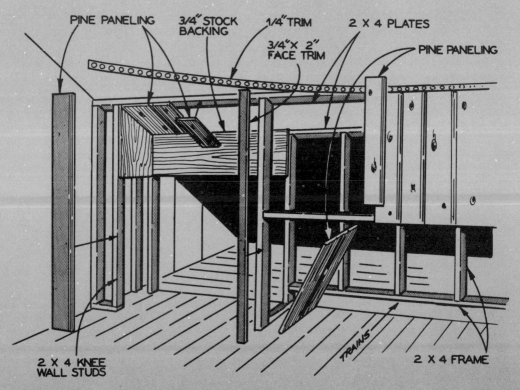

PINE PANELING · 3/4" STOCK BACKING · 1/4" TRIM · 3/4" X 2" FACE TRIM · 2 X 4 PLATES · PINE PANELING · 2 X 4 KNEE WALL STUDS · TRAINS · 2 X 4 FRAME

TYPICAL RECESSES FOR BOOKCASE, BED, AND CHESTS

were then blind-nailed so no marks would show.

To finish off the paneling, a strip of molding with a routed circle design was installed. Around the doors, half round molding was used to give the least possible place for dirt to settle. A tongue-and-groove pine flooring was then laid to provide a light surface in keeping with the rest of the room. To maintain the warmth of the knotty pine paneling, it was finished with clear varnish and paste wax. The floor was treated only with liquid wax which was buffed.

The only tools required for the whole job were a hammer, rule, level, miter box, rip saw, circular saw and an electric sander. A floor sander was rented. From the first nail to the last waxing, the project took seven months to complete. All the work was done on weekends and special days off; so, actually, the time involved was not too long.

The resulting room is light and cheerful and, at the same time, rugged enough to withstand the abuse that only a boy and his friends can inflict. One thing

Modern desk was moved into the study nook. The door leads to spacious closet.

verified in building this room is that careful planning pays off. Everyone who needs an extra attic room may not be in a position to plan so far ahead as we did, but a little extra time in the beginning will lead to a better and more satisfying job in the end.

Now our boy has his own room, secure he can invite friends without interfering with his parents. •

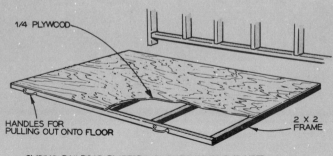

SLIDING RAILROAD PLATFORM DIMENSIONED TO SUIT NEED

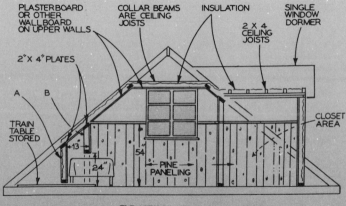

END VIEW OF ATTIC

COMPACT power booster (photo left) rides the brake master cylinder "piggy-back" style. Introduced on '59 Cadillac, Chevrolet, Mercury.

LESS brake "fade" and better cooling are among the advantages of wheel slots now on Chevrolet (photo right). Note how the smoke pot reveals heat escape in the photo.

Easy Does It by Fred Russell

Be sure you understand the power braking system on your car

POWER braking takes on a far simpler look when we stop to realize that the force that helps us stop our modern cars is none other than atmospheric pressure—that natural force of 16 pounds per square inch which presses against everything. We put it to work in a specific direction by exhausting the air in a special cylinder and then, by means of valves, allowing air pressure to push against a vacuum piston which is teamed up with the regular hydraulic braking system. Exhausting the power cylinder is accomplished by taking advantage of intake manifold suction.

Since there are nearly a dozen different variations of power braking systems it is important to know the one on your particular car, and stop thinking about those on your neighbor's pride and joy. Details vary widely, differences being due largely to engineers' desire to produce a trustworthy system compatible with a minimum of complications.

Some systems, for instance, employ what is known as a "slave cylinder," which is essentially an extra brake master cylinder that goes into action as soon as the car's regular master cylinder is activated by the driver pressing on the brake pedal. This is the feature found in the widely used Bendix Hydrovac system. In the Chrysler Corporation's bellows type system, as well as in its piston type, the slave cylinder is not used. Here the piston rod of the power cylinder pushes against the upper end of a pivoted brake pedal. When the driver presses against the pedal the power piston thus gives added movement to the master cylinder's push rod.

Newest in Bendix power braking is the Master-Vac, an extremely compact unit which operates in "piggy-back" manner with the master cylinder. It not only reduces pedal travel but pedal effort as well, lowering the pedal height to approximately that of the accelerator pedal.

A further difference in systems is the fact that some are of the "air-suspended" type. In the Bendix Tredlevac we thus find atmospheric pressure present on both sides

of the power piston when the brakes are not applied. For the pre-1955 models Buick used a "vacuum suspended system" which simply means that there is vacuum on both sides of the power piston when in the inactive stage, and while the engine or the vacuum pump is running. In this system there is an electrically driven pump to provide vacuum, should the engine not be running and the brakes need to be applied. Later, Buick switched to the "air suspended" system. Here, a vacuum reserve tank was installed in the vacuum line near the power brake cylinder.

A popular Ford and Thunderbird system is composed of a combination vacuum power cylinder, hydraulically actuated vacuum control valve, and a hydraulic slave cylinder, built into one compact unit. In another system—the Moraine— the power brake unit replaces the master cylinder only. Late model Chrysler cars have used a bellows instead of solid power cylinder. When the brakes are not applied

a return spring extends the bellows as they fill with air. Here the brake pedal is completely independent of the power system should the engine stall.

The best rule is to get a diagram of the system used on your particular car and become familiar with its details. The habit of inspecting the power system for leakage is important to good braking and safety. If the car has been in service for several years it is a smart idea to have a mechanic check the system's valves for signs of wear and scoring. If there is a vacuum pump in the system its oil supply should be checked every 5,000 miles. There's a filler screw on top of the pump. It will make a difference which brand of pump is on the car as to where to maintain the oil level—¼ inch below the cover top if it is a Morvac pump, one inch below the cover if it is a Trico. Speaking of oil prompts me to emphasize the fact that if you ever have occasion to take down a power cylinder for repairs be sure to guard all hydraulic system parts

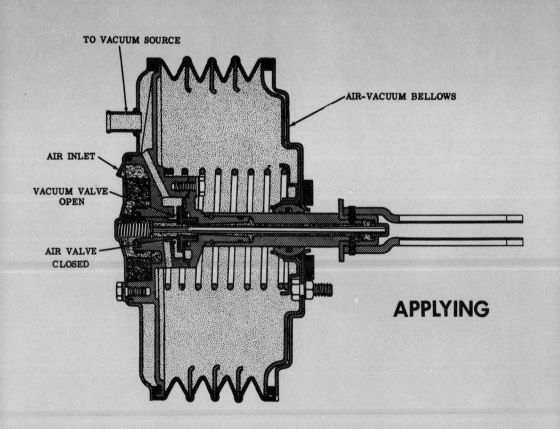

TO VACUUM SOURCE

AIR-VACUUM BELLOWS

AIR INLET

VACUUM VALVE OPEN

AIR VALVE CLOSED

APPLYING

from mineral oil or grease. Power cylinders or their air intake are fitted with an air cleaner which should be cleaned occasionally, especially when operating in a dusty area. Bleeding is different from conventional brakes. Better have specific instructions from the car maker here.

Packard cars which I drove back in the early 30's were equipped with power brakes, so I have had many years of opportunity to study their use. Contrary to the belief held by many drivers, they do not cause brake lining to wear faster, provided the brakes are not used to compensate for poor judgment. On long down-grades, power assistance usually saves the brakes, because the driver gets better results quicker when he holds down car speed and thus does not lapse into the bad habit of holding his foot on the pedal, even if only lightly. There is then less heating of the brakes, less risk of "fading" when the drums expand away from their shoes.

One thing is important to watch. Because the boosting action is so effective you may not realize that the brakes themselves may need attention. Don't let power be a cover-up for braking inefficiency. Check brake shoe clearances, and even if the brakes stop the car well after a few years of service, be sure to check to see if the lining is thick enough. Check brake fluid level frequently. In summer, brakes may operate at quite high temperatures when a car is traveling in fast traffic and has to make frequent high speed stops. Unless the fluid is of the finest quality—heavy duty type only—it may tend to vaporize. This would mean complete, though just temporary, failure. Pressure in the braking system is higher and that means more likelihood of fluid leakage. Always try to avoid overbraking, especially at low car speeds. Overbraking may jam one of the individual wheel cylinder pistons.

Easy does it. The aim is not to get a faster stop but an easier one. Response is also quicker and that means you have more space in which to bring the car to a halt. You need not brake so vigorously, therefore. One little point to guard against is the tendency many drivers have of not moving their right foot fully to the brake pedal. The right edge of their shoe sole may thus be pressing against the accelerator pedal. The effect is a sensation that the brakes are not working as well as usual. Men make this mistake more than women because of their wider shoes. Those wide brake pedals are a help here. Many drivers prefer to brake with the left foot. It gives quicker response but is likely to be a little more wasteful because often there is a tendency to brake against the accelerated engine or vice versa. •

CLOSE-UP of Chrysler vacuum booster shows unit applying power to lever which connects with master cylinder's piston.

RIGHT and left side views of Plymouth power brakes show how vacuum cylinder piston helps driver push down brake pedal.

YOKE

YOKE

VALVE OPERATING LEVER

PEDAL MOUNTING BRACKET

ADJUSTING CAM

POWER LEVER

BRAKE PEDAL RETURN SPRING

POWER LEVER

MASTER CYLINDER

MASTER CYLINDER

MASTER CYLINDER PUSH ROD

MASTER CYLINDER PUSH ROD

No More Spinning Wheels

The locking differential makes for better, safer driving

NOW that the differential has been glorified with a non-slip feature, it has moved up "front" in every driver's consciousness. Instead of allowing one of the rear wheels to start spinning when its tire fails to get traction on ice, or in snow or mud or sand, the new locking differential permits the automobile axle to transfer the major driving force to the wheel with the better traction. It not only prevents the car from becoming immobilized when one driving wheel loses traction, but also prevents wheel spinning when the car passes over particularly rough roads or nonuniform road surfaces.

You'll know the locking differential by various names such as Sure-Grip, Powr-Lok, Non-Slip, Twin-Traction, etc. In addition to maintaining differential action, this long-needed unit must also be able to transfer full torque to one axle shaft. In other words, it must not be a full-locking type and it must provide sufficient traction to the nonspinning wheel at all times and under all operating conditions.

There are some things about differentials and their care which should be considered before getting a line on how they work. For example, if the rear end becomes noisy when accelerating or when slowing down, it means there is faulty mesh between the pinion and ring gears. While tire noises may be mistaken for that made by the differential, tire noise varies widely when the car is traveling different kinds of road surface. This makes no difference with differential noise.

If you hear a knocking sound in the rear end, the chances are it is due to damaged or worn gears or trouble with the bearings. If there's any kind of noise in the rear end when the car goes around a corner, you can be sure it is due to trouble within the carrier that encloses the differential gears. Among conditions which will result in such noises are excessive backlash between the gears, or a differential pinion gear too tight on its shaft, or side gears of the differential too tight in the carrier.

What makes the differential so hard to understand is that we forget that its gears, which do the actual transferring of power to one rear wheel or the other, are carried within a carrier (sometimes called a case or a cage). Thus, if we look at an exposed rear axle in motion we can't see what the differential gears are doing unless the whole unit turns very slowly. The gear

carrier is bolted to the ring gear's side and rotates with it at all times when the car is in motion. The inner ends of the rear axles pass through the sides of this carrier but are separated from it by bearings. The differential pinion gears rotate on a shaft which runs at right angles to the axles and which are supported by the carrier. Finally, picture the differential gears meshing with the axle gears. All of this is enclosed within the rear axle housing with bearings to give the unit support and alignment.

Rereading this you will note that when the car is running straight ahead, with neither rear wheel lagging, the carrier of the differential rotates along with the ring gear, imparting rotational movement to both rear axles equally. The two little differential pinions do not revolve, even though they are twirling around in the carrier. It is like not turning a meat grinder even though you are whirling the whole thing around in a circle. When you slow down the right rear wheel, the gear on the inner end of the right rear axle also slows down. The two differential gears begin turning in opposite directions, thus sending the driving power to the gear for the left rear axle.

Similarly, when the car turns left there is lag or complete stoppage of the gear at the inner end of the left axle, and the differential gears again turn in opposite directions, but the reverse of the way they turned before. Pretty smart, these chaps who pioneered the gear-driven automobile!

Not to be outdone by the pioneers, engineers recently have evolved the new-type differential which provides automatic transfer of 80 per cent of the driving energy to the rear wheel which is favored with the better traction.

Special little friction plates are placed behind the differential gears for clutching the carrier to them. Four pinion gears are positioned within the carrier by two pinion shafts set at right angles to each other and having a loose fit at their intersections. But ends of each of these shafts have a pair of flat ramps which fit into ramps in the differential carrier. As a result of the ramping and clutching action, both axle shafts become clutched in the carrier, in proportion to the amount of torque transmitted. Thus, there is a check on any momentary tendency for the wheels to start spinning because of poor traction.

Too often we think of the differential as working only when the car is going into a curve or if one of the rear wheels can't get normal traction. But it is *always* in operation. With extra parts now in action in the newest differential, we must give this unit more consideration. Car makers are very emphatic about lubrication of the rear axle, some warning against changing the lube unless repairs are made, and all stressing the importance of keeping the lube level up. The nonslip differentials require a special lube. A hum in the rear end is usually an indication of low lube level and may also mean the wrong kind is being used.

What complicates matters is that modern rear ends are of the hypoid variety, in which the axis of the pinion at the rear end

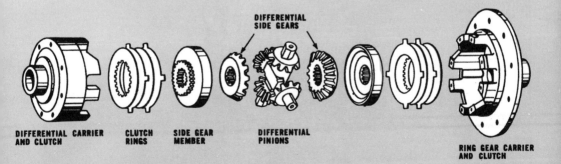

DIFFERENTIAL SIDE GEARS

DIFFERENTIAL CARRIER AND CLUTCH   CLUTCH RINGS   SIDE GEAR MEMBER   DIFFERENTIAL PINIONS   RING GEAR CARRIER AND CLUTCH

COMPONENTS of non-slip differential are shown above. Picture on opposite page shows application: main flow of power is transferred to right rear wheel, which has traction; the left rear wheel, which is on ice, receives little power and therefore does not spin.

of the propeller shaft is below that of the ring gear. There is thus a sort of whipping action of the gears, with extremely high pressure between them. A hypoid axle helps make for a lower car without loss of road clearance. But the gear stress is terrific when you consider how much torque can be thrown to this unit from a high horsepower engine, teamed with an automatic transmission.

While the ring gear digs up plenty of EP (extreme pressure) lube as it turns through the housing's supply, it also can force foreign matter directly into the differential gears if lube isn't clean. In addition to paying close attention to lubrication you can prolong the trouble-free life of the differential (any kind) by avoiding jackrabbit starts. Slower speeds over rough roads will save differential gear wear because there will be less action of those little pinions when the wheels are alternately slowed down and accelerated. In the case of the new nonslip differential, you'll be saving wear on four of the little pinions plus the friction clutches.

Testing differential gears for backlash is a slow job involving use of a dial indicator. But some motorists can go a lifetime of cars without ever needing to have this done. You can easily test for differential noise while the car is being used, however. Pick a smooth asphalt road which reduces

tire noise to a minimum. Drive ten miles or so to warm up the gears. If noise develops, note about how far down you press the accelerator. Stop the car and accelerate the engine to the same speed to make sure the noise isn't due to the exhaust. To make certain you are not hearing tire noise, shift to neutral and allow the car to coast from 40 mph or thereabouts back to 15.

Bearing noises are more continuous than those made by gears and do not change much as speed changes. A bearing noise can best be described as a sizzling or crackling. Gear noise always changes as car speeds change. Sometimes we have a combination of both noises.

It may also develop that the differential has been damaged by excessive backlash in the drive line. Here the real culprit would be worn universal joints. Don't overlook the rough action of an automatic transmission as a cause of differential disturbances. A little "klunk" from the transmission when putting the selector lever into Drive or Reverse with a cold motor is normal enough, but watch out for rough downshifting.

With the simple differential going out of the picture, and the more complicated nonslip type taking its place, we must give this department of the car more attention than before. Take it easy and watch your lubrication. •

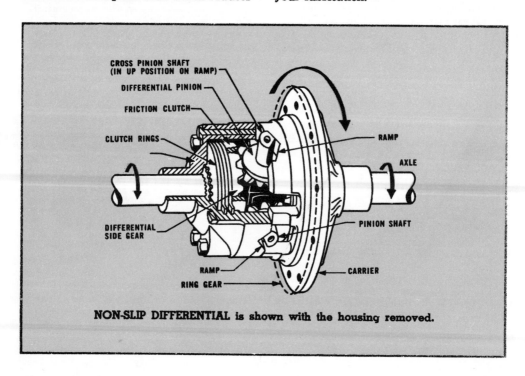

CROSS PINION SHAFT
(IN UP POSITION ON RAMP)
DIFFERENTIAL PINION
FRICTION CLUTCH
CLUTCH RINGS
RAMP
AXLE
DIFFERENTIAL SIDE GEAR
PINION SHAFT
RAMP
CARRIER
RING GEAR

NON-SLIP DIFFERENTIAL is shown with the housing removed.

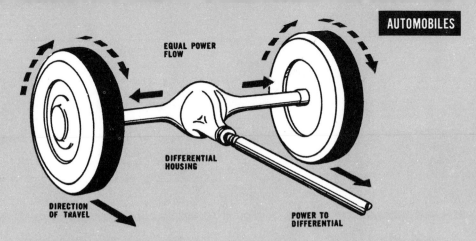

EQUAL POWER FLOW

DIFFERENTIAL HOUSING

DIRECTION OF TRAVEL

POWER TO DIFFERENTIAL

WHEN DRIVING STRAIGHT, either in forward or reverse, there is equal torque or power flow to each wheel with both the ordinary and non-slip differential.

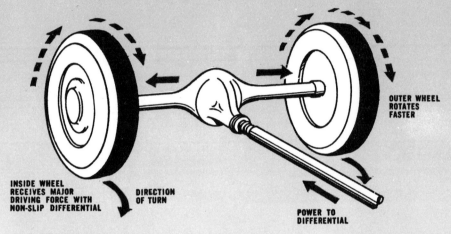

OUTER WHEEL ROTATES FASTER

INSIDE WHEEL RECEIVES MAJOR DRIVING FORCE WITH NON-SLIP DIFFERENTIAL

DIRECTION OF TURN

POWER TO DIFFERENTIAL

WHEN TURNING, the outside wheel rotates faster than the inside wheel. This is an action which is normal with either the ordinary or non-slip differential.

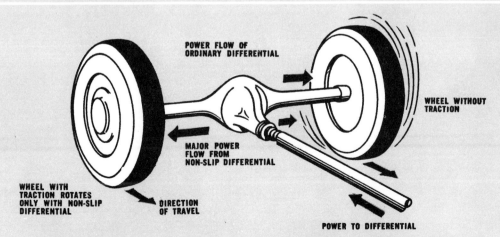

POWER FLOW OF ORDINARY DIFFERENTIAL

WHEEL WITHOUT TRACTION

MAJOR POWER FLOW FROM NON-SLIP DIFFERENTIAL

WHEEL WITH TRACTION ROTATES ONLY WITH NON-SLIP DIFFERENTIAL

DIRECTION OF TRAVEL

POWER TO DIFFERENTIAL

SLIPPING WHEEL just spins with ordinary differential; non-slip differential applies driving force to wheel with traction, prevents spin of opposite wheel.

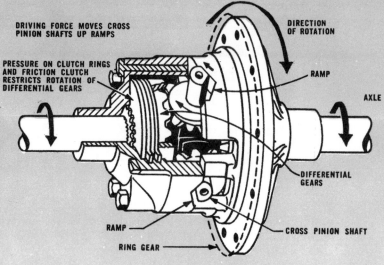

DRIVING FORCE MOVES CROSS
PINION SHAFTS UP RAMPS

DIRECTION
OF ROTATION

PRESSURE ON CLUTCH RINGS
AND FRICTION CLUTCH
RESTRICTS ROTATION OF
DIFFERENTIAL GEARS

RAMP

AXLE

HOW non-slip differ-
ential operates if a
car is being driven
in a straight line.

DIFFERENTIAL
GEARS

RAMP

CROSS PINION SHAFT

RING GEAR

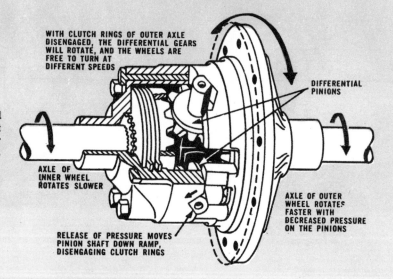

WITH CLUTCH RINGS OF OUTER AXLE
DISENGAGED, THE DIFFERENTIAL GEARS
WILL ROTATE, AND THE WHEELS ARE
FREE TO TURN AT
DIFFERENT SPEEDS

DIFFERENTIAL
PINIONS

BOTH WHEELS will
rotate at different
speeds when the car
is turning a corner.

AXLE OF
INNER WHEEL
ROTATES SLOWER

AXLE OF OUTER
WHEEL ROTATES
FASTER WITH
DECREASED PRESSURE
ON THE PINIONS

RELEASE OF PRESSURE MOVES
PINION SHAFT DOWN RAMP,
DISENGAGING CLUTCH RINGS

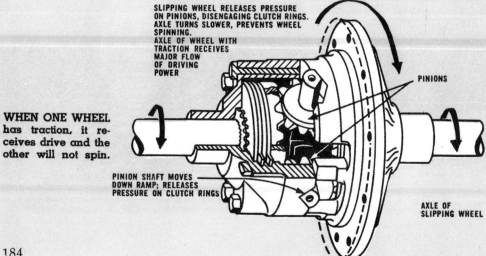

SLIPPING WHEEL RELEASES PRESSURE
ON PINIONS, DISENGAGING CLUTCH RINGS.
AXLE TURNS SLOWER, PREVENTS WHEEL
SPINNING.
AXLE OF WHEEL WITH
TRACTION RECEIVES
MAJOR FLOW
OF DRIVING
POWER

PINIONS

WHEN ONE WHEEL
has traction, it re-
ceives drive and the
other will not spin.

PINION SHAFT MOVES
DOWN RAMP; RELEASES
PRESSURE ON CLUTCH RINGS

AXLE OF
SLIPPING WHEEL

YOUR CAR may not control from the middle like this Cornell-Liberty Safety Car, but with a non-slip differential you're safer than you are with a regular rear axle.

ILLUSTRATION at the right shows standard rear end with the housing unit removed.

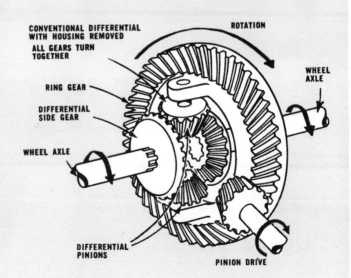

CONVENTIONAL DIFFERENTIAL
WITH HOUSING REMOVED

ALL GEARS TURN
TOGETHER

ROTATION

WHEEL
AXLE

RING GEAR

DIFFERENTIAL
SIDE GEAR

WHEEL AXLE

DIFFERENTIAL
PINIONS

PINION DRIVE

Check Those Wheel Bearings

No wheel is any better than the bearings in it

A S NO CHAIN is stronger than its weakest link, so no wheel is better than its bearings. Long before the front wheels of your automobile let out a squeal to warn of need for lubrication, the bearings can be causing a variety of troubles—some of them a threat to your security. The bearings in the rear wheels, however, are sealed and often last the life of the car.

Because front-wheel bearings are not considered in the thousand-mile car lubrication, they are often overlooked until something happens. A driver can land in a ditch because a wheel bearing overheats and breaks. Even though the affected wheel doesn't fail, the car can develop such a violent shimmy at 70 mph the driver just isn't prepared to meet the challenge. Another serious mishap may occur because a wheel bearing is merely loose, not broken. This sort of thing causes too much play in the steering wheel. On the surface it doesn't seem much to worry about, but too much play is likely to cause the driver to over-steer in trying to correct this condition.

DEFECTIVE BEARINGS can be detected by a crackling sound when the wheel is spun.

EXCESSIVE SHAKE may be due to loose bearings though there are other causes.

LOOSEN wheel nuts before jacking car or removing nut on steering knuckle spindle.

PRY OFF the grease cap to get at the nut at the end of the steering knuckle spindle.

Overtight bearings can be just as much a hazard, being one of the leading causes of road weave or wandering. That is why it is so important to know how to adjust wheel bearings professionally. Even if you don't do the job yourself, you can be sure the mechanic entrusted with the work is on the ball. Nothing rolls like a car that has well-adjusted bearings. It even affects braking.

There's no general agreement as to how often front-wheel bearings should be lubricated. Many engineers believe that every 10,000 miles would be about right, but if you are thinking in terms of inspection it would be smart to check twice a year. This may not call for removal of the bearings but a check to see if they need tightening. If they need more than a little taking up probably there is reason for the abnormal looseness. Has the car been striking curbing? Was the wheel bearing lube the right kind in the first place? Were the wheels accurately adjusted when the bearings last received attention?

It helps us get a clearer picture of today's needs in this important department of car care to think back to the days before there were brakes on the front wheels. Remember how we used to relubricate the wheel bearings? Just filled the little hub cap with a batch of fresh cup grease and screwed it back on. The old grease was automatically forced out the inner bearing around the wheel spindle. Wipe it off and the job was complete. Not only were the bearings given new lubricant, but they were fairly well cleaned in the bargain. But today we must remove the wheels to change the lube. In fact, we must be careful that the grease retainer is in good shape, otherwise grease may get through into the brake. Lube must

be the special fiber type for this particular job, otherwise overheating might thin it out and encourage leakage into the brake. With the high cost of today's brake work there can be no running risks.

Front-wheel bearings may be of the ball or the roller type. On each front wheel there is an inner and an outer bearing, these serving to support the hub on the steering knuckle spindle. To get at these bearings it is necessary to remove the wheel with the hub and drum assembly, and for convenience some folk like to take off the wheel and tire to lessen weight and to facilitate handling. Removing the wheel tire assembly is necessary if the bearing cups need to be replaced. Remember here to loosen the wheel stud nuts before jacking the car. Block the diagonally opposite wheel before setting the jack.

With the wheel cover off, pry off the metal cap at the end of the spindle, thus uncovering the spindle nut which can then be removed after bending and withdrawing the long cotter pin which holds it in position. Next spread clean newspapers or a large clean cloth on the garage floor and be careful not to let the outer bearing fall when you start pulling off the wheel. The inner bearing will remain in position because it is held by the oil seal packing. Removing this packing will make it easy to take out the inner bearing.

There is a cup for each of the two bearings in each front wheel. A real inspection should include examination of these cups. Should anything abnormal appear after all the old grease is wiped from the hub and the spindle the cups may need to be replaced. For this operation it is necessary to use a punch to drive out the cups with special care. Start the new cup squarely

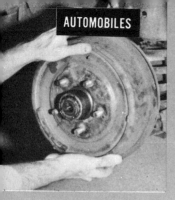

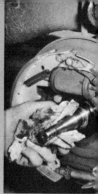

LEFT TO RIGHT: Take care not to drop outer bearing when pulling the wheel from the spindle. Next, take out oil seal and remove inner bearing. Then wash bearing in gasoline or kerosene and clean the spindle.

into the hub so as to avoid distortion and the risk of cracking it.

There is some difference in bearing types for front wheels, and for that reason it is well to have the car maker's specific instructions. Don't be confused by the loose way in which the terms "cones" and "races" are used. A tapered roller bearing runs over a cone-type inner race. Races in front-wheel ball bearings are actually cones to permit adjustment. One late-model car uses a dust seal at the inner end of the spindle and features a radio static collector at the outer end just inside the metal grease cap. Cones or complete bearings must be free to creep a bit on the spindle. Purpose of this is to provide for a constantly changing load contact between them. The spindle should always be polished and bearing lube applied as a means of accelerating this creeping and to prevent rust from forming.

Right here put it down as car care gospel the fact that you should never *add* grease to wheel bearings. If the supply is found

to be short, or if it appears emulsified, the grease should be completely removed and replaced. This prevents forcing old grease into the inner bearing and possibly past the retainer. It provides the important opportunity to inspect bearings, cones and cups.

The experienced mechanic will wash all parts in a solvent such as unleaded gasoline or kerosene and thoroughly dry them off. It is necessary to dry them because wheel bearing lubricant won't adhere to oily surfaces. Also, only in drying the parts will he be able to decide for sure whether he has cleaned them thoroughly.

We watch him as he checks for flicking, cracking, "brinelling" or excessive heat. Those less technical about it would settle for noting if parts show any wear, pitting or roughness. Note, too, how he packs the bearings without applying any excess of grease. Short-fiber wheel bearing grease is his selection for this job. On his car he adds 2½ ounces to the inner surface of the hub. Another mechanic may use a bearing

NEW OIL SEAL is usually required; drive it squarely so as to avoid any distortion.

AFTER CHECKING inner bearing and replacing oil seal, hub is put on spindle.

WHEN SPINDLE IS CLEAN, remove all old grease and grit from raceway in the hub.

GREASE the spindle and then work new lubricant into wheel hub and both bearings.

packer, but our friend gets along fine by hand. He carefully removes all excess grease, when sure that the bearings are going to be well protected, and puts a light coating of lube on the spindle. Some car makers consider it unnecessary to pack the hub, suggesting merely that a light coat of grease be applied to the inside surface to prevent rusting.

The inner bearing assembly should be placed in its cup with care taken to make sure that the new seal is squarely driven into the hub. This is the way to prevent distortion. In the case of a ball bearing, the inner bearing cone should be installed in the oil seal, not placed on the spindle, otherwise the seal would be damaged when putting on the wheel. When the wheel is replaced, the outer bearing is then set into position. Its cone comes next, then the safety washer and the spindle nut.

Now for the actual adjusting of the bearings. First, the wheel must be properly and completely seated on the spindle. If a torque wrench is used, Cadillac suggests

setting up the nut to about 18 lbs-ft to insure proper seating of all parts and to make sure the threads are free. Then the nut is backed off and retightened to four lbs-ft. Buick suggests a simple way to obtain the same results without a special wrench. The nut is tightened until the bearings are preloaded at least one hex; then it is backed off until the bearing is slightly loose. Either plan helps make certain that the bearings are seated.

The final step is to retighten the spindle nut until all bearing looseness disappears. The nut is then lined up to the nearest cotter pin hole and the pin is slipped in. Now spin the wheel, remove the cotter pin and repeat the job of tightening. Sometimes as the grease works in it will change the picture enough to cause wheel looseness which, in turn, may cause noise that will be amplified by the car's front end. On a rough road a slightly loose bearing may sound like something broken or very loose in the steering systems. It's wisdom to watch your wheels. •

OVERTIGHTEN nut after outer bearing and washer are replaced; this seats bearings.

BACK OFF NUT just enough so that wheel will spin free without bearing looseness.

Maybe It's Carburetion

Carburetor trouble often involves more than just the carburetor

WHEN the engine misbehaves and you are faced with the problem of checking into carburetion trouble, keep in mind that the story concerns much more than the carburetor itself. The whole fuel system may be involved. That covers everything from the cap on the fuel tank filler pipe to the intake manifold.

When the engine of his car failed to keep running without pumping on the accelerator, one motorist discovered that there was a bad air leak around the intake manifold system. This was leaning the mixture so that even with the choke valve closed there wasn't normal cold motor operation. Often failure of the engine to start properly is due to a too low carburetor float level. More frequently it is the result of too low fuel pump pressure. If fuel escapes into the intake manifold or percolates from the carburetor when the hot engine is switched off for the night, any weakness of the fuel pump will show up the next morning as a very sluggish start. It is simply that the pump is tardy refilling the carburetor float bowl.

Much starting delay is caused by the choke valve not closing sufficiently, and we get into a lot of warm-up trouble with the choke opening sluggishly. An engine that is under-choked will pop back through the carburetor intake when accelerated. If it is overchoked it will buck and load up. To help maintain a more uniform pressure these days many motorists are using pressure regulators in place of the conventional filter. Regulators also filter, and the latest is an adjustable kind that enables the car owner to experiment a bit if carburetion doesn't seem to be just right.

Modern carburetors are complicated in the extreme, and only the most skillful mechanics are qualified to tamper with them. The four-barrel type carburetor is

COMPLICATED and efficient, carburetor needs an occasional cleaning to function properly.

THE AUTOMOBILE FUEL SYSTEM
Showing Typical Locations Where Entrapped Moisture Can Cause Trouble

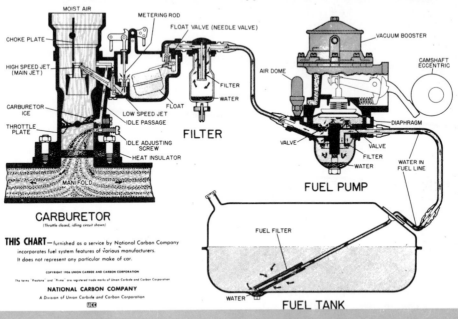

MOIST AIR

METERING ROD

FLOAT VALVE (NEEDLE VALVE)

VACUUM BOOSTER

CHOKE PLATE

CAMSHAFT
ECCENTRIC

HIGH SPEED JET
(MAIN JET)

AIR DOME

FILTER

WATER

CARBURETOR
ICE

FLOAT

LOW SPEED JET

IDLE PASSAGE

DIAPHRAGM

THROTTLE
PLATE

VALVE

VALVE

IDLE ADJUSTING
SCREW

FILTER

HEAT INSULATOR

WATER

WATER IN
FUEL LINE

FILTER

MANIFOLD

FUEL PUMP

CARBURETOR
(Throttle closed, idling circuit shown)

FUEL FILTER

THIS CHART—furnished as a service by National Carbon Company
incorporates fuel system features of various manufacturers.
It does not represent any particular make of car.

COPYRIGHT 1956 UNION CARBIDE AND CARBON CORPORATION

The terms "Prestone" and "Prime" are registered trade-marks of Union Carbide and Carbon Corporation

NATIONAL CARBON COMPANY
A Division of Union Carbide and Carbon Corporation

WATER

FUEL TANK

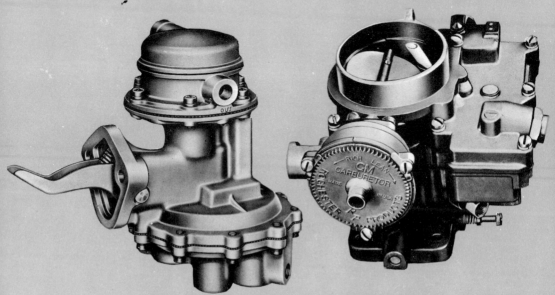

THIS FUEL PUMP has extra diaphragm in order to boost vacuum windshield wipers.

MUCH CAR TROUBLE is due to the need for readjusting the automatic choke control.

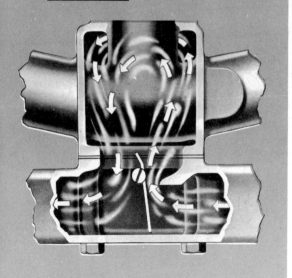

UNLESS the manifold heat control valve closes when the engine warms up, the gas mileage and performance of car will drop.

quite popular, and we have many engines with twin four-barrel carburetors. A newer development is the use of three carburetors, arranged so that for economy the center unit is used to provide for normal car operation. Progressively the other two come into the picture as power and sustained higher speeds are required. Common to modern carburetors is the float system. Then there are the "circuits" for idling, part throttle and power. There is also provision for fast idling. There's the choke system and the unloader. Some carburetors have a "dashpot" control to slow down throttle closing where the driver lifts his foot suddenly from the accelerator for a slow-down with cars equipped with an automatic transmission. This helps prevent stalling during such slow-downs.

There are many details and refinements. But certain facts stand out regardless of the carburetor's make and model. One is the interesting discovery that troubles with the carburetor usually come on gradually. And much of this trouble is due to dirt and gummy deposits in the jets and passages. This can be removed with special solvents. Never use wire to clean out restrictions in jets. Mechanics use compressed air or blow into the jets by mouth. Dirt is best kept out of the carburetor by greater care in checking the air filter and by making sure to empty the fuel filter bowl periodically. Incidentally, when cleaning the filter bowl

take care not to leave any lint. Some of this may get into the carburetor to unseat the needle valve in the float chamber.

Best way to keep water out of the fuel system is to aim to keep the gas tank filled at all times. Stop off on the way home to fill up with gas. This helps prevent condensation. Never run with the tank low because the pump may draw in dirt and water even if the tank is equipped with a filter at its outlet. Some mysterious cases of engine failure have been traced to a clogged vent for the tank. This vent may be in the cap or in the filler pipe. If there is a special pipe running from the tank to the filler pipe to help prevent spilling over when gasoline is pumped into the tank rapidly, make sure that it is not broken off where it enters the filler pipe. Road dust can be kicked up by a rear tire to gain entrance into the tank this way. Fine sand will actually pass the filters and get to the carburetor to cause stalling.

There is little a car owner can do about the fuel pump except to make sure its cover is tight and to be suspicious of any leakage of gasoline. Pumps may be inclined to fail after 25,000 miles of hard driving. Pressure may actually rise if the pump's diaphragm hardens with age. Diaphragms are more likely to fail at high speed in hot weather. If the pump has a booster side for improving vacuum windshield wiper action the tip-off of trouble is slowing down of the wipers on hills. The engine may also run rough at slower speeds in High with a conventional transmission or in Drive just before downshifting if the gears are automatic.

One unit of the carburetion system that is frequently overlooked is that short length of fuel line between the pump and main line. It is flexible to take care of the shaking of the engine in its flexible mountings. Leakage is likely at its connections or in the mesh of the line itself. No fuel will leak out but air can be sucked in. This creates a condition similar to vapor lock, and may stall the engine. Best rule is to replace this flexible fuel line whenever buying a new pump.

Where the engine has seen a lot of service its intake manifold should be cleaned of gummy deposits. Always make sure manifolds are tight and see that there is no leakage where the carburetor bolts to the manifold. If the engine stalls during the warm-up period this is likely due to ice forming on the throttle plate. Best remedy is to let the engine fast idle to warm it before starting off. •